Towards a Green Architecture

Six Practical Case Studies

Brenda and Robert Vale

© Robert and Brenda Vale 1991

RIBA Publications Ltd
Finsbury Mission, Moreland Street, London EC1V 8BB

RIBA Publications is the publishing company of the
Royal Institute of British Architects

Editor: Alaine Hamilton

ISBN 0 947877 47 9

Design and computer page make-up by Penny Mills, Coventry
Printed and bound by Hollen Street Press, Slough

Contents

Acknowledgements

We would like to thank the following people, institutions and companies for their help, without which these case studies could not have been written.

Strathclyde
Dr. John Twidell, Director of the University of Strathclyde Energy Studies Unit, and Dr. Robert Forrest and Dr. Callum Stuart who form the monitoring team for the building; Graham Roddick, Deputy Director, University of Strathclyde Estates Office; The Kennedy Partnership, Architects; Kaiser Bautechnik; Abacus Simulations Limited.

Easthall
Colin Porteous, Mackintosh School of Architecture, Glasgow; Easthall Residents Association; Community Architecture Scotland; Heatwise Glasgow.

Spectrum 7
John Doggart and Richard Ferraro, ECD Partnership, Architects.

Two Mile Ash
Dr. Paul Ruyssevelt, formerly of the Polytechnic of Central London, now at Halcrow Gilbert.

NMB Bank
Ton Alberts, Alberts en van Huut, Architects; Mr. H. Majoor, Treffers en Partners; NMB Bank Corporate Public Relations and Publicity Department. Special thanks go to Bill Holdsworth for arranging for us to visit the Bank, and for providing so much help and information.

Woodhouse
Woodhouse Medical Centre Co., for commissioning the building.

Introduction

The end of the 1980s coincided with an increase in awareness throughout the world of the problems associated with the environment. It became impossible to open a newspaper or turn on the television set without being reminded of global warming, pollution, rainforest destruction, acid rain or the growing hole in the ozone layer. This public awareness, combined with the statements made by politicians, who increasingly had to be heard making the right noises, especially after the Green Party won 15% of the votes in the UK elections to the European Parliament in 1989, might suggest that environmental problems are just another 'bandwagon' issue, which will soon disappear from the public consciousness. The question that must be asked before any discussion of a possible 'green architecture' can begin is whether environmental problems are important, or whether they will go away if they are ignored.

Damage to the environment was apparent in the nineteenth century as the industrial revolution got under way, and writers such as William Morris and John Ruskin inveighed against the negative effects of unbridled capitalism. The greenhouse effect and acid rain were both predicted by nineteenth century scientists, as were energy shortages and the problems of unrestrained population growth.

Ozone damage

One problem unique to the latter part of the twentieth century that was not predicted by the Victorians is the damage to the ozone layer in the Earth's atmosphere caused by the group of chemicals called chlorofluorocarbons (CFCs). Invented in the 1930s as safer refrigerants, they have found widespread use in air-conditioning plant, refrigerators, fire extinguishers, aerosol propellants and as the foaming agents for plastics insulants. The fact that they could damage the earth's ozone layer was predicted in the early 1970s, but the effect was assumed by the UK Government to be of no significance for a hundred years [1].

Other countries were less sanguine: Oregon, for example, banned aerosols containing CFCs in 1975 [2]. It was only when a 'hole' was discovered in the ozone layer over Antarctica in the late 1980s that the problem was taken seriously. The ozone layer screens out the damaging ultra-violet radiation from the sun, and life on earth could not escape from the oceans until the layer formed millions of years in the past. The damage to the ozone means that more ultra-violet radiation can get through to the Earth's surface. CFCs and related chemicals have already destroyed about 3% of the world's ozone screen in the last 20 years. The US Environmental Protection Agency predicts that a 5% reduction in ozone will lead to 360,000 additional cases of skin cancer across the world [3].

About 50% of the world production of CFCs is used in buildings, either as refrigerants, fire extinguisher systems or in foamed insulation (of the commonly used materials, only expanded polystyrene is CFC-free) [4]. CFCs pass very slowly up through the atmosphere into the ozone layer, where they break down to their basic constituents, one of which is chlorine. A single atom of chlorine can help destroy 100,000 ozone molecules [5]. This means that even though the use of these substances will be stopped by the year 2000, it will be another 30 years before the level of damaging chlorine in the atmosphere is back down to the 1986 level, and many years longer before the ozone layer is no longer suffering damage from their use [6].

If CFCs are to be taken out of use, it will be essential for architects to act by refusing to specify them and by suggesting alternative materials or different design strategies. Manufacturers are already helping by redesigning materials and systems to use less hazardous materials for refrigerants or the foaming of insulation boards.

As environmental problems go, the reduction in the use of CFCs is a relatively simple problem to solve; governments have acted together to agree to phase them out globally by the year 2000; the chemical companies who manufacture CFCs need to develop less hazardous alternatives; aid needs to be given to developing nations to enable them to manufacture these substitutes. The problem is basically a matter of finding, and then applying, a suitable 'technical fix'. The governments of the world have finally agreed that the banning of CFCs is necessary, and they have come together to do it, albeit not as rapidly as many atmospheric scientists would wish.

The elimination of chlorofluorocarbons from the atmosphere is probably the simplest of the world's environmental problems; there are technical solutions to it that are reasonably straightforward – and they can be applied, given the will to apply them.

Destruction of forests

At a more complex level, but one that affects architects in their daily activities, is the matter of the tropical rainforests. These are being cut down for their timber, and more extensively to clear land for ranching or agriculture. The rainforests play a major role in the earth's carbon cycle, taking carbon dioxide out of the atmosphere and producing oxygen, and they are also a vital reservoir of biodiversity. Architects can help by specifying only those tropical hardwoods that come from sustainably managed plantations [7]. Even if the trees cut down have no economic value, they may still be cut down to clear the land, but they will be burned instead of being sold, and this will liberate huge quantities of carbon dioxide, adding to global warming. If the countries where the forests are located see their destruction as necessary to improve their economic condition, the developed nations will have to provide aid to offset the economic disadvantages of keeping the trees intact. Again, the solution is a matter of international will and international aid.

Carbon and the atmosphere

Ozone depletion and rainforest destruction are probably the only two major environmental problems that are not linked inseparably to energy consumption. The use of conventional fuels to supply the world's growing demand for energy is adding about 6 billion tonnes of carbon per annum to the atmosphere [8]. The total quantity of carbon in the atmosphere at present is about ten times less than the total amount locked up in the known reserves of fossil fuels. If these reserves are burned as fuels, the carbon content of the atmosphere will increase tenfold, with unimaginable consequences for all life on the Earth.

Carbon enters the atmosphere as carbon dioxide, produced when fuels containing carbon are burned. Coal, wood, natural gas and oil all contain carbon, and all produce CO_2 in use. The only fuel that can be burned without carbon dioxide production is hydrogen, which burns to produce water. In the atmosphere, CO_2 combines with other gases such as methane, nitrous oxides and CFCs to create the so-called greenhouse effect. The gases in the atmosphere allow solar radiation to pass through to warm the surface of the

Earth, but they impede the outward passage of heat energy from the surface into space. The net result is a rise in temperature, as more heat is coming in than is escaping.

There is now general agreement among the world's climatologists that the greenhouse effect is happening; what they disagree about is how fast it is occurring and what the effects will be. The general range of global temperature rise that is predicted for the coming forty years is in the range of 1·5 to 4·5°C. This may not sound very much, but the global average temperature during the last Ice Age was only 4° less than the temperature now. It is clear that apparently small changes can have enormous consequences [9].

The most obvious result of the greenhouse effect is that an increase in global average temperatures will lead to a decrease in the ice at the poles. This process may be accelerated by negative feedack: the ice is white and reflects some of the radiation from the sun back into space without contributing to the heating of the Earth. If more ice melts there will be more dark water area to absorb more solar radiation, which will in turn increase the temperature so allowing more ice to be melted, and so on.

A similar mechanism is suggested for the permafrost areas of North America and the Soviet Union. Increasing temperatures will start to melt the permafrost, allowing the escape of massive quantities of methane, a gas with a global warming potential thirty times greater than CO_2, which will rise into the atmosphere and add to the greenhouse effect, increasing the global temperature and so melting more permafrost [10]. Not only is the effect of increasing temperature hard to predict, it is also impossible to say how rapidly the process may occur.

One way of taking carbon out of the air is to grow trees and plants. Growing plants use atmospheric carbon dioxide as well as soil nutrients, and the carbon is locked up in the structure of the plant, released only when it rots or is burned or eaten. One way of reducing CO_2 is to plant trees in enormous quantities wherever possible. It is suggested by the Oak Ridge National Laboratory in the USA that a forest the size of the United States (not including Alaska) would be needed to absorb 50% of the CO_2 emitted globally by the burning of fossil fuels. It would require each person on earth to plant, and care for, four tree seedlings per year [11].

However, the pollutants put into the air by fossil fuel combustion, particularly the sulphur dioxide from coal-fired power stations and the nitrous oxides from vehicle exhausts, dissolve in the rain to form dilute sulphuric and nitric acids. These fall on the trees that should be taking up the carbon and kill them. A large proportion of Germany's forests are dead or dying because of acid rain [12]. Fossil fuels are not only adding carbon dioxide to the atmosphere, they are killing the trees that might take it out of the atmosphere again. At the same time the tropical rainforests are being felled even though they have not yet been damaged by acid deposition.

The answer seems simple: the world must reduce its energy consumption. But while energy consumption needs to fall, world population is rising. The United Nations predict that the present population of rather more than 5 billion will rise to about 8 billion, even with concerted efforts to limit it. They calculate that the world could probably manage to feed about 11 billion people [13]. All these extra people will consume energy. Developing countries will need to increase their energy consumption to allow what the United Nations calls 'sustainable development'. They will not expect to remain in poverty and starvation. Even if the developed world cuts its use of fossil fuels by 50%, world energy demand will rise because of the increasing demands of the developing countries, anxious to have their share of the resources that the richer nations have tended to keep to themselves.

At the start of the 1970s, when a United Nations conference on pollution and the environment was held in Stockholm, it was assumed that fossil fuel reserves, particularly of oil and natural gas, would run out in about forty years' time. The greenhouse effect was appreciated as an additional problem, but one that lay far in the future.

At the beginning of the 1990s the greenhouse effect is acknowledged as the major problem, leading to the ironic reversal that the world cannot afford to burn up all the reserves of fossil fuels because of the amount of carbon that this would put into the atmosphere. The end result is the same, in spite of the change in the perception of the problem. The use of fossil fuels must be reduced or even abandoned.

The western nations have an obligation to set the pace in this matter for at least two reasons. First, the developing world in the short-to-medium term may need to increase its use of fossil fuels in order to achieve a situation where people have the basic amenities of life, such as adequate water, food, shelter and sanitation. If world energy consumption is to be stabilised, the west must make cuts in order to permit others to make increases. Second, the western countries have one quarter of the world population, but consume three quarters of the energy [14]. They are the biggest energy consumers and the biggest polluters in per capita terms. It follows that they must be seen to change before they are in any position to try to tell the rest of the world what to do.

Saving energy

It may seem an impossible task to reduce the energy consumption of a country without causing suffering. The proponents of nuclear power in Great Britain used to say that without nuclear power, the population would be 'freezing in the dark'. Energy is such an essential component of all activities that any reduction in its use would seem to lead to inevitable hardships. In reality, the situation is rather different. People consume energy not for its own sake but for the services it provides: heating a room, running a refrigerator, or having a motoring holiday. If the same activities and services can be provided by using less energy, no one would have any objections or feel that they were enduring any suffering.

That equal services can be provided is indisputable. In electric lighting for example, it is possible to replace the tungsten filament incandescent light bulbs that most people use in their homes with compact fluorescent bulbs. These give out the same amount of light with an 80% reduction in electricity use. An in-built electronic ballast in the latest types ensures that the light does not flicker. As far as the user is concerned, the service provided is the same whether the bulb is tungsten or compact fluorescent.

The compact bulbs also last eight times longer than the incandescent ones, so that even in financial terms the compact bulbs show a clear benefit. Although each one costs fifty times as much as a normal bulb, its running costs are so low that when it comes to the end of its life the total costs involved in buying and running it will be less than half those for conventional light bulbs.

In North America, these benefits are realised to the extent that some electricity generating companies are giving the compact fluorescent bulbs free to their customers to reduce demand, because this is much cheaper than building and operating new power stations. It is worth looking at the light bulb issue in some detail, because it is a clear example of all the benefits of energy efficiency. Every bulb used immediately saves energy; it saves the user money, it reduces the output of carbon dioxide and it lessens the emissions that lead to acid rain. What can be demonstrated by a simple light bulb applies across the whole world economy. Efficiencies can be achieved in all sectors.

The role of the architect

In the United Kingdom about two thirds of the total energy consumption is attributable to the construction and servicing of buildings [15]. It is interesting that the Department of Energy estimate [16] that renewable sources of energy have the technical potential to meet half the current UK delivered energy demand. As a profession architects are uniquely placed to aid in the reduction of energy demand and therefore of global warming, because they are responsible for such a large slice of the total cake. If they do not take an active interest in energy conservation, the world's environmental problems will not be solved.

There are several ways in which architects can begin to influence the energy demands of the built environment. Some of them can be achieved at no cost. For example, buildings can be oriented towards the south to benefit from solar gain, and windows can be enlarged on the southerly elevation and reduced in size on the north. On open sites, shelter belts of planting can be used to deflect or divert the wind away from the building. These simple climate-responsive measures can have worthwhile energy-saving benefits [17].

The specification of non-CFC insulating materials and European or tropical hardwoods from sustainable sources are now accepted as part of the repertoire of an environmentally-aware designer. The next step is for architects to start to specify materials in terms of their environmental impact. Information is becoming increasingly available on the energy used to make various building materials, and on their effects on the health and well-being of builders, users and the rest of the world [18].

The specification of environmentally-benign materials can be extended to the design of buildings for a long life; it is inefficient to regard buildings as disposable items. In the energy crisis of the 1970s the RIBA coined the slogan 'Long life, loose fit, low energy' to describe the approach that architects should adopt to design. This slogan is still valid. Long-lasting buildings that can be adapted for new purposes, and the adaptation of old buildings, are both essential parts of a green approach to design.

Finally, architects must address seriously the issue of designing buildings for energy efficiency. It is no longer enough to satisfy the Building Regulations, which in the UK are some of the worst in Europe from the environmental point of view. The 1990 version, supposedly upgraded, calls for thermal standards that were mandatory in Sweden in 1930, yet southern Sweden has a climate comparable to that of Newcastle-upon-Tyne. A serious attempt must be made to design buildings that minimise fossil fuel consumption for space heating, hot water, lighting, ventilation and power. Ways must be found to convert existing buildings to similar standards. It would be possible, through the efforts of architects alone, to reduce energy demand in Britain to the point where renewable sources could provide it all.

The examples shown in this book are all buildings that demonstrate architects' attempts to go beyond the norm in tackling environmental problems. In various ways they offer extreme solutions to problems that too few yet perceive as extreme. It is to be hoped that they will not remain isolated examples, but will point towards a new direction for architecture as part of global recovery.

References

(1) Department of Environment (1976), *Pollution Paper No.5*, 'Chlorofluorocarbons and their effect on stratospheric ozone', HMSO, London.

(2) Papanek V. and Hennessey J. (1977), *How things don't work*, Pantheon Books, New York.

(3) Hoffman J.(1988), *Future concentrations of stratospheric chlorine and bromine* (EPA 400/1-88/005), United States Environmental Protection Agency.

(4) Curwell S., Fox R., March C. (1988), *Use of CFCs in buildings*, Fernsheer Ltd., London.

(5) Boyle S. and Ardill J. (1989), *The greenhouse effect*, New English Library, Hodder & Stoughton, London.

(6) Brown P. (1990), 'World unites on ozone deal', *The Guardian*, 30 June 1990, London and Manchester.

(7) Friends of the Earth (1988), *The good wood guide*, London.

(8) Boyle and Ardill, *op. cit.*

(9) *Ibid.*

(10) *Ibid.*

(11) Marland G. (1988), *The prospect of solving the CO_2 problem through global reforestation (DoE/NBB0082)*, United States Department of Energy.

(12) Pearce F. (1986), 'The strange death of Europe's trees', *New Scientist*, December.

(13) The World Commission on Environment and Development (1987), *Our Common Future*, Oxford University Press.

(14) *Ibid.*

(15) Energy Efficiency Office (1990), 'RIBA Conference discusses greenhouse effect', *Energy Management: Journal of the Energy Efficiency Office*, Department of Energy, London.

(16) Department of Energy (1988), 'Renewable energy in the UK: the way forward', *Energy Paper No.55*, HMSO, London.

(17) Dodd J. (1989), 'Greenscape: (2) Climate and form', *Architects' Journal*, 19 April 1989.

(18) Curwell S., March C. and Venables R. (Eds.) (1990), *Buildings and Health: the Rosehaugh Guide to the design, construction, use and management of buildings*, RIBA Publications, London.

Halls of Residence,
Strathclyde University, Glasgow

Strathclyde University is one of two universities in Glasgow. Its campus is near the centre of the city, with student residences located close to the departmental buildings and lecture theatres. A recent student residence, first occupied in November 1989, uses a technique new to the UK to provide space heating by means of solar radiation. The building is interesting as an example of the nearest that 'green architecture' has yet approached 'intelligent building'.

Passive solar design

The key to the energy performance of the Strathclyde building, the largest in the world to utilise this technique, is the combination of greatly reduced energy demand with the use of transparent insulation. In a 'conventional' passive solar building, radiation shines through glazing (usually double or triple) and is stored as sensible heat in a dense structure that forms the walls, floor and ceiling of the space. The classic example in Britain is the extension to St. George's School in Wallasey, near Liverpool, designed in 1961 by Emslie Morgan. This has walls of 225mm brickwork and a concrete roof slab, all insulated on the outer face with 125mm of expanded polystyrene so as to store the heat in the mass. The entire south face is double glazing, and the building section is arranged to give maximum southern exposure while minimising that on the north. The result is that the building is heated by solar radiation, by heat from the incandescent lights, and by body heat from the pupils, and requires no additional heating plant, although one was installed for emergencies [1].

The south elevation

(photograph: Alastair Gardner)

One of the problems of the classic passive solar approach is that the glazing needed to admit the radiation that warms the building is a poor insulator. Whereas the current UK Building Regulations require a U-value of 0·45 W/m²K for a wall element, a single glazed window has a heat loss rate over ten times greater, with a U-value of 5·7 W/m²K. Depending on the gap between the panes, double glazing may reduce this to 2·8 [2] and triple glazing will be 2·0, but these elements are still very poor in performance terms compared with a reasonably well insulated wall or a roof. This means that the conventional passive building will be losing heat through its large glazed areas at night and, when the solar radiation levels are low, at a much greater rate than through the solid parts of the construction. The areas of glazing may be much greater than needed for daylighting alone, in order to maximise radiation gains, and this exacerbates the problems of possible temperature extremes and glare.

Transparent insulation

In an attempt to improve the situation, researchers have been trying to find a material that would be transparent to incoming short wave solar radiation, while minimising heat loss outwards from the building – the so-called transparent insulation material, or TIM. Work over many years both in Israel and at the Fraunhofer Institute in Freiburg, Germany, has resulted in a material that has some of the required properties. The material used at Strathclyde is made in Israel and systems to make use of it have been under development at the Fraunhofer Institute since 1981. It is a honeycomb structure of transparent polycarbonate, and can be likened to a lot of thin-walled transparent drinking straws stuck together to form a slab. In use it is positioned with the straws aligned horizontally at right angles to the plane of the wall of the building [3]. Each straw has a diameter of about 2mm. Currently available materials are reported to have a U-value of 0·66 W/m²K for a 100mm thick layer, while allowing transmission of 56% of the solar radiation [4]. The honeycomb structure of the material, its very thin walls and the fact that it is transparent allow solar radiation to penetrate, but reduce convective, conductive and radiative heat flow outwards.

In use, solar radiation passes through the TIM and heats the mass wall behind it, but the insulation material reduces the flow of heat from the wall to the exterior. The nature of the material is such that direct solar radiation is not necessary; indirect radiation from an overcast sky is sufficient to provide useful heat, leading to the concept of 'heating by daylight'. The heat stored in the wall passes to the interior of the building. Measurements made in Germany on a south-west facing façade in November show the temperature of the internal wall surface varying one or two degrees either side of 20°C, while the external surface rises to nearly 40°C on a sunny day [5]. Walls incorporating the new material can be shown to have a negative U-value [6] because they gain more energy than they lose, with an overall contribution of between 100kWh and 200kWh per square metre of TIM wall area over the heating season, depending on geographical location [7]. This would suggest that a well insulated house could have its entire space heating demand met by a 50m² TIM wall.

The use of transparent insulation requires the incorporation of additional design features compared with a traditional wall. The work of the Fraunhofer Institute has concentrated on the design of the whole wall to make the use of the transparent insulation a practical proposition. A wall that collects energy and acts as a source of heat in winter will not be wanted during the summer, and a way must be found to prevent overheating. This is controlled by the use of a

The section shows diagrammatically the construction of the transparent insulation wall. Reading from left to right:

A pane of low-iron content glass in glazing bars.

A cavity containing a motorised blind which can be raised to admit solar radiation (lower dotted arrow) or lowered to reflect unwanted solar radiation in summer (upper dotted arrow) or to conserve heat at night.

Transparent insulation material and supporting clips.

Backing sheet of transparent polycarbonate to prevent convection losses through the insulation from the heated wall.

Cavity to prevent conduction losses through the insulation from the heated wall. The cavity is closed horizontally at intervals to reduce air circulation leading to higher convection losses.

Layer of dark blue paint to increase heat absorption into wall.

Wall of dense concrete blocks to store heat.

Internal plaster finish.

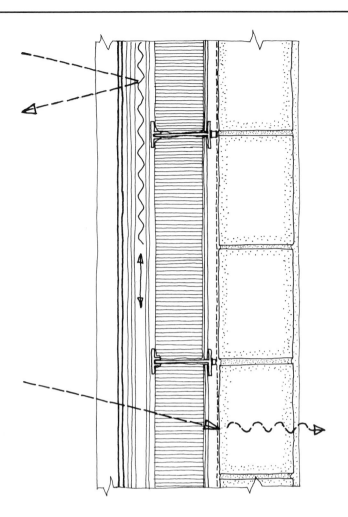

motorised blind, which is lowered over the face of the insulation to exclude unwanted radiation. The blind also offers increased insulation at night. In the long term the wall construction must exclude the potentially damaging effects of dust and atmospheric pollution, which may reduce the transparency of the insulation.

The construction of the complete wall therefore follows the following pattern:

1) outer glazing, preferably with maximum solar radiation transmission, which necessitates glass with low iron content. The glazing needs framing and supports, all of which must remain waterproof;
2) motorised blind, with access for maintenance and repair;
3) transparent insulation material;
4) glass or transparent plastic back layer to lessen convection currents through the TIM;
5) air gap to minimise heating of the TIM by conduction of heat from the thermal storage wall;
6) dense wall with absorbing surface such as black paint [8].

Clearly this is a complex structure compared with a conventional wall. Like any building element, the TIM wall will be expected to have a long life and to require little maintenance. Whether these requirements are compatible with the incorporation of motorised blinds and control systems in the external walling will be discovered only by experience.

The Strathclyde approach

The German firm, Kaiser Bautechnik, has worked closely with the Fraunhofer Institute in the development of TIM technology. The University of Strathclyde appointed Kaiser as developer for the construction of new student accommodation, and Kaiser appointed a local firm of architects, G.R.M. Kennedy & Partners, to carry out the detailed design of the new buildings. The arrangement follows normal practice in Germany. Kaiser offered two forms of design-and-build: in one, the construction costs are paid by the developer who then leases the building to the client. In the other, the client pays directly for the construction and owns the building, and Kaiser Bautechnik act purely as developers, saving the client from the problems of seeing the project through to completion. The latter approach is the one adopted at Strathclyde [9].

The Strathclyde student residences are on an ideal site for solar exposure, a long south-facing slope. They are arranged in four long blocks running east–west: two on the upper edge of the site, separated by a narrow gap, and two more at the bottom of the slope. The planning conforms to classic passive solar principles, each narrow single aspect block has student rooms on the south side with service spaces, such as kitchens and bathrooms, on the north. In total there are rooms for 376 students, with groups of eight rooms served by a staircase, again located on the north side. The blocks are five storeys high, but the steep slope means that the entrances are not necessarily at ground level, reducing the height of stairs to be climbed. There is no lift, which is at least a saving of energy. Kitchens, common rooms, showers and wcs are provided at a ratio of one of each per four students, and washbasins are provided in the shower and wc rather than in individual rooms.

The unobstructed southerly exposure maximises solar gain

(photograph: Robert Vale)

The elevation to the street, facing north

(photograph: Robert Vale)

The construction of the blocks follows the interior planning, with the north elevations in brick with small windows to minimise heat loss. The construction is conventional, with brick cavity walls, but the inner leaf is of dense concrete block to maximise thermal storage capacity, and there is a 150mm cavity filled with mineral fibre insulation, giving an overall U-value of 0.22 W/m^{2}K [10]. From the outside the southern elevations are a curtain wall of glazing. This is somewhat misleading, because seen from inside an individual student room the south-facing wall reads as solid masonry with a window in it. The solid areas either side of the windows are where the TIM walls are located.

From the outside the building has two very different faces. The north wall, fronting on to Rotten Row in the case of the upper blocks, matches to some extent the University's other student residences (or at least the more recent ones) on the surrounding campus. It is in a lightish red brick (Maltby Denver Red from Nottingham Brick) and is subtly detailed with overtones of both Scottish baronial architecture combined with hints of Mackintosh. Particularly striking are areas where the wall projects in a very shallow curve. The result is to enliven what is by necessity a large and relatively unperforated surface, something akin to a Glasgow version of Ralph Erskine's famous wall at Byker.

By contrast, the curtain-glazed south wall is more regular, although here too the architects have angled and curved it to break the monotony. This also means that the individual rooms have considerable variety in both aspect and plan, with no two rooms in a group having the same plan form. Two are more or less triangular, but different: one is square, and one has an angled south wall. This all helps to break the usual monotony of the standard student cell, as does the grouping of rooms into recognisable 'flats' of four with their associated service facilities. Blue paint has been used on the dense blockwork behind the transparent insulation, rather than the black which might have been expected, and this can be seen through the transparent insulation behind the glazing. The framing for the glazing is also blue, as are the spandrel panels below the windows. The blue wall has the slight disadvantage of making discoloration of the transparent insulation due to dust and dirt very visible.

Above these walls, Scottish on one side and solar on the other, sits a roof of pale green profiled aluminium sheeting enclosing the hot water systems and other plant. Described as being in the 'Nissen-hut style [11], it is fashionably curved on the north elevation, but on the south incorporates a suitable slope for the siting of solar collectors for hot water provision, should that be deemed desirable in the future.

The individual student rooms have built-in furniture to compensate for their small size. Made of varnished softwood, it incorporates curved planes, odd angles and wooden poles that run from floor to ceiling to create a feel reminiscent of a stylish vegetarian café. Each room contains a bed/sofa, a desk, a wardrobe, shelves and a seat with built-in storage.

The communal spaces are more conventionally fitted out. The kitchens have standard cupboard units with a cooker and sink, fridge and freezer, but here too there are purpose-made dining chairs and tables to carry through a sense of commonality with the bed-sitting rooms. Finishes are generally painted plaster, and the overall impression is of robust finishes that will wear well and be easy to redecorate.

On the north elevation the windows of the heated rooms are triple-glazed with a low emissivity coating, and have the large sections and massive fittings that make British 'high performance' windows seem so flimsy by comparison. On the unheated communal stairs the windows are single-glazed in colour-coated metal frames. Walls between the rooms and the stair are insulated to the same standard as the external walls, and each group of rooms is separated by a door from the stair. This seems in line with the traditional treatment of stairs in Glasgow tenements and walk-up flats.

Windows and blinds

On the south side the windows are double-glazed and low-E coated and arranged in a vertical row in the curtain wall with insulated spandrel panels containing 50mm mineral fibre insulation. The windows can all be opened, and those in the student rooms incorporate a number of complex (and expensive) features. The most obvious one is a blind made of low-emissivity coated fabric and decorated with a pattern of well-known Glasgow buildings, giving an impression of a view out of the window even when the blind is closed. The blinds are operated by motors, with a manual switch in each room for opening and closing. They are closed automatically at 6 pm and can be opened again by the occupant of the room, if desired, but they then close again at 10 pm. Anyone who wants to gaze at the stars can then open the blind again with the switch, but by closing them, the control computer is determinedly sending the message that the blinds ought to be shut. If the energy targets of the building are to be met, it is important that as many blinds as possible are shut for as many of the hours of darkness as possible. The programming of the closing period can be changed easily to allow for seasonal variations.

Space heating is minimised by the highly insulated construction, and assisted by the TIM wall which occupies varying proportions of the wall of each bed-sitter, depending on its location in the plan. The elevation on the south has been chamfered and angled to provide some visual variety, and this means that some rooms have no TIM wall and rely on direct solar gain through their windows, which are in consequence triple-glazed. Whether this will have any effect on the temperatures reached in those rooms will be discovered in due course. In some rooms, bookshelves are provided on the south-facing TIM wall, and these will tend to reduce heat transfer from the wall to the space.

Back-up heating

The structure of the building has a very high mass with a dense concrete block inner leaf to the cavity walls, concrete floors and masonry partitions. These all store heat and also provide good soundproofing and fire resistance. There is no heating provision in the service rooms, but the sanitary accommodation is in the centre of the plan with very few external walls. In the student rooms, heat to back up the TIM wall is provided by a 200W electric heater. This can be switched on by the student, but all heaters are automatically turned off by a pulsed control system after a maximum of four hours. The period of the cycle is independent of the switching-on time of any particular heater, leading to the situation that an individual's heater may turn off almost immediately after it is turned on – or it may stay on for nearly four hours. Students may find this system rather confusing, but instructions and explanations are provided in each room. Each student room also has a 60W desk light, the only light fittings in the building that do not use compact fluorescent lamps, and a student (of varying heat output according to metabolism and activity but, say, 110 Watts) when the room is occupied. In this respect the building is similar to Morgan's classic model at Wallasey, and the total available heating output of 370W is adequate for a well-insulated room with only one external surface.

Hot water is supplied to each group of four rooms on five floors by a 20kW hot water boiler (gas-fired but not condensing) mounted in the roof space supplying water to a pressurised loop system. This means that the hot water is constantly circulated by a pump through a circuit off which are all the hot water outlets. The advantage is that there is no delay in running off hot water; it is always hot. The hot water pipes are to be lagged to reduce uncontrolled heat gains, since a 15mm diameter pipe running from floor to ceiling has the same surface area as a radiator about 300mm wide by 400mm high. (In fact this is similar in size to the radiators used in the Woodhouse Medical Centre, see Case Study 6).

The building is ventilated by opening the windows, but it is also fitted with heat recovery units in the kitchens. The heat exchangers are mounted above the kitchen cupboards and provide an extract over the cooker, and from the shower room and wc. Fresh air is supplied to the kitchen and the hall. There is a booster control which can be operated manually to clear the kitchen of the fumes of some culinary disaster, and it also operates when the shower or wc are in use (triggered by the light switch) with a 20 minute overrun. Tests are being made to see the effect of reducing the overrun time, as the unit is noisy in boost mode, and to date it has been cut to only a minute with no ill effects. Sound attenuators have been tried in the ducts, which also incorporate filters, but there are still some problems with noise.

The heat recovery system runs continuously 24 hours a day, and is essential in a well-sealed and densely occupied building. In practice it is likely to recover up to 70% of the heat in the outgoing air. Some problems occur from the fact that the ventilation system does not extend to the individual student rooms, which can be ventilated only by opening the window, and thereby losing heat to excess.

Problems and possibilities

The Strathclyde student residences are a fascinating example of the application of some of the ideas of intelligent building to the pursuit of green architecture. The computer system monitors solar radiation, external wall temperature and air temperature, and adjusts the external blinds accordingly to absorb or reject heat, changing the appearance of the façade. The window blinds are also controlled as described earlier.

There have been some problems with the building, but these seem to be the kind of problems to which any new building is subject. Not surprisingly, on a project of this complexity, the building was not completed in time for the returning students at the start of a new academic year, and many had to go into temporary accommodation. Once the students had got into the new residence there were some complaints of condensation. Excess moisture is to be expected in a new building, and in the case of one that incorporates so much masonry and concrete there is bound to be a lengthy drying-out period. Experience of other high-mass buildings with high levels of insulation suggests that it may take as long as a year for the structure to dry out and reach thermal equilibrium. Residual condensation problems, if they occur, might be tackled to some extent by linking the heat recovery control to humidistats in the showers and wcs, rather than to the light switches. The lack of ventilation in the student rooms, other than by the opening of windows, which is counter-productive in an energy-saving building, could be remedied by providing further heat recovery systems, but they would need to be fitted with fire dampers in the ductwork. Another possibility might be individual through-the-wall heat recovery units giving individual control in each room.

The building was occupied before the blinds were fitted to the TIM wall and this, combined with a heatwave in the spring of 1990, led to overheating, with temperatures of 56°C on the external surface of the heat storage wall, and as much as 36°C on the internal surface. This is undoubtedly an inconvenience, but once the blinds are fitted it will be avoidable. At least the heat has helped to accelerate the drying-out process.

Detail of the TIM wall

(photograph: Robert Vale)

More interesting than the temporary problems, which are not inherently different from the problems that occur on any new building, are the more long term and even philosophical aspects of the building and its approach to resource conservation. On the practical level, how robust are the systems that it contains? The motorised blinds have got to work reliably year after year, yet in a car it always seems to be the electric windows that fail first. Will it be straightforward to replace the blinds as and when necessary, and how will this cost compare with the cost of the fuel saved by the TIM wall compared with a more conventional (in green architecture terms) direct gain passive building with a superinsulated structure? Will atmospheric dirt and diesel fumes affect the transparent insulation material in the long term, by reducing its transparency?

The building uses electric heating in the student rooms because it is cheap to install and, more important, easy to control. In England, electricity for space heating cannot be considered 'green', being the most CO_2-intensive form of space heating if derived from fossil fuels. However, in Scotland, 60% of electricity is made from non-fossil fuel sources (hydro-electricity and nuclear) [12], so electric back-up heating in this instance can be seen as appropriate, and part of the building's response to site and context.

In time these questions will be answered, as will others that have not yet been asked. The Energy Studies Unit at Strathclyde University are monitoring the building and have instrumented two complete 'flats' to give a record of the temperatures achieved, and the consumption of conventional fuels. The results of their monitoring will show whether the TIM system is cost-effective in practice, and time will show whether it is robust enough in operation.

Perhaps of greater interest is whether the approach is acceptable to the users. The idea of a student room where the blinds close automatically over the window at a fixed time on a winter's evening may not be to everyone's taste. Although the designers of the system have incorporated every possible manual override, some users may find the whole idea of this degree of automated control unusual. Thermal control by means of thermostats is common, and no one thinks about it because it is invisible, but the Strathclyde building is unusual because the control alters the room and its relationship with the exterior. The acceptability of this degree of control by an external system may depend ultimately on the degree to which the general public are prepared to accept the importance of energy-saving, and its relationship to the reduction of environmental problems. Certainly there have been no complaints from the residents about the automatic blinds.

The Strathclyde student residences are the largest building in the world to make use of transparent insulation technology to allow indirect solar radiation to be used for space heating. This is a technology that could have considerable benefits if it can be shown to be sufficiently robust in daily use. Not least of its attractions is the potential for retrofitting to existing solid-walled buildings to provide insulation, heating and waterproofing in one new cladding. This aspect alone makes the student residences interesting, but they also represent an attitude to the use of technology and controls that goes a stage beyond what is in common use at present.

Strathclyde University is worthy of praise for being the first place in the world to try out this new technology at a large scale. Additional funding to pay for the increased capital cost of approximately 20% was provided by the European

Community's Energy Demonstration Scheme, and the Scottish Development Agency. The university's Energy Studies Unit is also providing the detailed monitoring that will help to demonstrate whether the student residences are either an interesting but isolated experiment, or the first step in a completely new approach to building design for a resource-conscious age. What the world needs is more organisations with the vision to give support to the full-scale trial of promising new technologies.

Clients: University of Strathclyde
Architects: G.R.M. Kennedy & Partners
Design-and-build contractor: Kaiser Bautechnik (Director of Architecture, Peter Henderson)
Contractor: G.A.
Group Monitoring: University of Strathclyde Energy Studies Unit (Director, John Twidell; Researcher, Bob Forrest)

References

(1)   Hawkes D. (1987) 'Energy revisit: Wallasey School: pioneer of solar design' *Architects' Journal* Vol. 185 no. 18, May 6, pp55–59.

(2)   Her Majesty's Stationery Office (1990), *The Building Regulations 1985 Approved Document L1 Conservation of fuel and power, 1990 edition*, HMSO, London.

(3)   Goetzberger A. (1989), 'Transparent insulation: a new solar energy component', 2nd European Conference on Architecture, 4–8 December 1989, Paris.

(4)   Bollin E. (1989), 'One year experience with a solar house with transparent wall insulation (TWI)', 2nd European Conference on Architecture, 4–8 December 1989, Paris.

(5)   Wagner A. (1989), 'Renovation of a one-family house with transparent insulation', 2nd European Conference on Architecture, 4–8 December 1989, Paris.

(6)   Forrest R.J., Twidell J.W., Stuart C.F. (1990) 'Transparent insulation – student residences in Glasgow' *Proceedings of the 1990 Conference North Sun*, Pergamon Press.

(7)   Stahl W., Bollin E., Schmid J., Vahldiek J., Voss K., Wagner A. (1989), 'Wall heating with transparent insulation – results from realized demonstration projects', 2nd European Conference on Architecture, 4–8 December 1989, Paris.

(8)   Stahl *op. cit.*

(9)   Ridout G. (1989), 'Living daylights', *Building*, 18 August 1989.

(10) Edwards B. (1990), 'Vorsprung durch Kaiser Bautechnik', *Architecture Today*, No. 6, March 1990.

(11) Ridout *op. cit.*

(12) Twidell J. (1990) personal communication.

Easthall Flats,
Easterhouse, Glasgow

Post-war housing

Following the second world war, the traditional building materials for housebuilding were in short supply. At the same time there had been an enormous increase in productive capacity to produce the apparatus of war, and these factories were suddenly no longer needed for the manufacture of armaments. There was also a massive demand for new housing, both to replace the dwellings destroyed by enemy action, and to provide homes for the returning service personnel following demobilisation. As at the end of the first world war, there was a rapid increase in novel methods of housebuilding that would make use both of the spare factory space and of available materials.

Several systems were developed using precast concrete elements to build the walls of houses. One of these was the Wilson block, developed by Wilson's Terazzo Manufacturing Company Ltd of Glasgow [1]. The Wilson system used a single prefabricated concrete element to create a cavity wall. The blocks had an inner leaf of 65mm-thick concrete and an outer leaf of 50mm, joined by steel ties that were encased in concrete and gave a cavity of 100mm. Various versions of the blocks were developed with slightly differing leaf thicknesses. The principle of the blocks was that a cavity wall could be constructed in half the time because the inner and outer leaves were built at the same time, using a unit no heavier and containing no more concrete than a conventional 100mm-thick block. The method therefore offered savings of both labour and materials compared with traditional construction.

As part of its post-war slum clearance programme, Glasgow Corporation built four huge peripheral housing estates; one of them is Easterhouse. With a population of about 50,000 in about 15,000 dwellings it is the size of a substantial town. Unlike many post-war estates, Easterhouse is comprised of traditional dwellings, in the form of three-and four-storey tenement blocks with staircase access. Some are of conventional brick cavity wall construction, some

The front elevation
(photograph: Robert Vale)

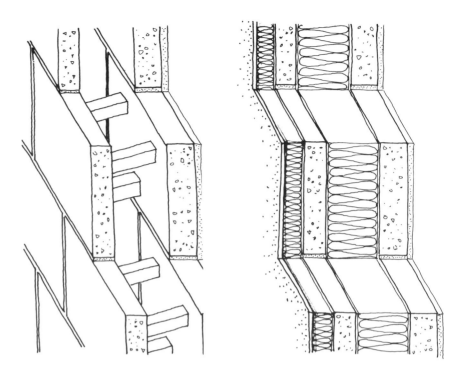

Before: the Wilson Block wall as built showing the 50mm thick outer leaf, the 100mm cavity with concrete encased ties, and the 65mm thick inner leaf with plaster finish.

After: the wall as upgraded, with external self-coloured render on 50mm insulation to provide waterproofing, plus 100mm mineral fibre blown into cavity.

have an external leaf of concrete blocks with a brick inner leaf (so-called terrazzo block construction) and some are of Wilson blocks.

Problems of deterioration

The tenants of Easthall, a neighbourhood of Easterhouse, participated in the formation of the Easterhouse Anti-Dampness Campaign in 1982, by which date the problems of the estate were becoming increasingly apparent. In 1984, Easthall Residents Association (ERA) became a member of the newly established Technical Services Agency (TSA). TSA was set up as a user-controlled technical aid centre providing, among other things, technical advice to tenants' groups on dampness, condensation and fuel poverty. Controlled by a management committee consisting largely of tenants, it obtained Urban Aid funding enabling it to employ both architects and administrators on a full-time basis.

TSA carried out a survey and analysis of 18 houses on ERA's behalf [2]. In the Wilson block houses, mortar had fallen out of external joints allowing moisture penetration, and the U-value of $2.43W/m^2K$ made heating very difficult for tenants on low incomes. The poor performance of the construction combined with the lack of efficient heating systems to produce a situation in which tenants were paying up to eight times as much to achieve comfort conditions as those in more recent and efficient homes. Since most tenants were unable to afford such bills, the result was underheated buildings and consequent problems of condensation, mould growth and ill health. Following this report, ERA requested a temperature monitoring programme with the help of the Community Resources Project at Glasgow College of Technology (now Glasgow College). Results confirmed the thermally sub-standard nature of the houses, with extremely low temperatures in rooms other than the living room [3].

Tenants' action

The solutions to the problems apparent in the Wilson block flats were the result of a complex but ultimately successful combination of tenant pressure and professional expertise. It is worth describing the process to give an indication of the time and effort put in by all those involved, and especially by the tenants themselves.

A typical block of Wilson Block
construction

(photograph: Robert Vale)

The situation in the mid-1980s was that the Scottish Solar Energy Group
(SSEG) wanted to promote a passive solar ideas competition in Scotland to
encourage architects and others to appreciate the potential of solar energy in a
northern climate. At the same time, the West of Scotland Energy Working
Group (WSEWG), funded through the Glasgow Institute of Architects, wanted
to run a competition to look specifically at methods for the thermal upgrading
of sub-standard housing. The third participant was TSA, whose aim was to use
community architecture methods to provide improved thermal conditions for its
member groups in Areas of Priority Treatment designated by Strathclyde
Regional Council [4].

At the start, WSEWG wanted to use 1970s deck access blocks for its thermal
upgrading competition. The Competition Committee of the Royal Incorporation
of Architects in Scotland (RIAS), who were acting in an advisory capacity, felt
that a more generic house type would be preferable, as it would produce
solutions of greater applicability. ERA, having already worked closely with
TSA over a period of two years, were enthusiastic about the idea of a
competition using as its basis their blocks of three-storey flats, some built of the
infamous Wilson blocks.

At the suggestion of Dr. David Bartholemew, then directing research into passive
design at the Energy Technology Support Unit (ETSU) based at Harwell, it was
decided to hold the competition as a weekend event during which participants
would work in teams to produce their designs following a day of lectures and
discussions relating both to the problems they were to address and the kinds of
solutions that might be appropriate. Initially it was planned to stage the event at
an academic institution, but in the end funding was not forthcoming from official
agencies, who were perhaps put off by the political implications of the tenants
being centrally involved in the organisation of the whole competition. The final

outcome was that ERA hosted the event themselves, with money and help in kind from SSEG, WSEWG, TSA and the local authority. Timetabling, organisation of venues, catering and other aspects were handled entirely by ERA.

The event was called Heatfest, and was held at the end of January 1987 in Easterhouse, using various community halls and meeting rooms. It attracted participants from all over the UK, including public and private sector architects, architecture students, academics, quantity surveyors, engineers, housing managers and repesentatives from tenants' groups in the west of Scotland [5]. The first day was a formal conference, in which a number of noted academics and practitioners talked about the problems and available techniques that might be useful in the design of solutions. Participants at the event paid a fee which allowed tenants and students to be subsidised.

In fact the conference attracted even more people than the competition itself. At the close of the conference session the organisers allocated people to teams to work on the next stage. Each team included at least two tenants, one acting as chair (ERA themselves could not compete since they were the hosts), architects and students, and at least one other person with a related skill, such as a services engineer or a housing official. A quantity surveyor was on hand for cost advice, and the conference speakers and ERA members acted as 'floating' advisers, going round the various groups. In all, there were seven teams.

Each team was issued with a briefpack containing maps, technical data about the flats, and a list of Project Objectives. In addition, the pack included a simple tabulated calculation procedure, to allow each team's design proposals to be compared both with the flats as existing, and with each other. The first day ended with visits to see the flats, followed by dinner and a ceilidh in the local church. The next day the teams spent the day working on their designs. On the final day of the Heatfest, each team's ideas were presented to the assembled company, first by a tenant, and then by an architect.

The adjudication panel comprised three of the expert speakers from the first day: Tom Markus, Dean Hawkes and Owen Lewis, plus one person from each of four appraisal groups representing different interests – tenants, landlord (the local authority), architects and energy specialists. Final choice of the winning scheme was announced at a follow-up meeting in March, attended by most of the original participants.

The Heatfest idea generated much enthusiasm from those who participated. It broke down barriers, both real and imagined, between tenants, students and professionals but, more important, it led to the formation of a detail design team made up of tenants, architects, academics, students and other professionals. In a series of regular meetings this team produced a package of design measures that could be applied to flats in Easterhouse, in the rest of Glasgow and in other cities.

In 1983 an organisation had been set up in Glasgow called Heatwise. It was funded by a variety of sources: Manpower Services Commission, Glasgow District Council, Department of Health and Social Security, Department of Energy and the EEC Social Fund [6]. The aim of Heatwise was to tackle fuel poverty and unemployment by providing energy advice and an insulating and draughtproofing service. This work had in fact already been carried out in

New conservatory spaces
at the rear

(photograph: Robert Vale)

Easthall, and was thus the existing baseline case from which Heatfest
competitors had to work. Heatwise were represented in the Heatfest detail
design team (the similarity in names was coincidental), and had also by that
time initiated an Urban Aid-funded 'Jobs and Energy' project with the aim of
promoting more radical thermal upgrading through a series of pilot projects. It
seemed fortuitous to exploit the Heatfest solution as the first Jobs and Energy
pilot project, and subsequently a Pilot Project Sub-committee, chaired by a
representative of the ERA, was set up to supervise the project.

Funding was provided by Heatwise themselves in conjunction with a considerable
number of public and private sector organisations and companies [7]. Architects
for the scheme were Community Architecture Scotland (CAS), which had been
set up by the Technical Services Agency as a community business to carry out
projects of this type for tenants and other community groups.

The brief for upgrading

The original brief for the Heatfest stipulated the following objectives:

'1. Modify the building fabric in order to reconcile the space heating load for all flat locations to thermal comfort within an affordable expenditure band, taken to be an average house temperature of 18°C within an upper cost limit of £5 per annual week.

2. Provide a well distributed heating capability, the criteria being the unit cost in relation to (1), responsiveness and quality/comfort.

3. Devise a natural/mechanical ventilation system which is simple to control and economically promotes adequate rates of air change to negate adverse effects of normal pollutants and condensation risk, ie healthy ventilation without draught nuisance and within an energy-conscious framework.

4. Suggest modest planning improvements where these relate to energy efficiency and moisture production, eg internal clothes drying provision.

5. Suggest improvements externally, with emphasis on energy saving potential.'

It was also stressed with respect to (1)–(5) that credit would be given to energy-saving techniques which simultaneously enhanced the visual quality and amenity of the internal and/or external environment. [8]

The measures have been applied as follows to the demonstration block, 9 Edderton Place, Easterhouse.

The solutions
(1) Insulation

The biggest problem was the Wilson block walls which were damp through moisture penetration as well as condensation. The lack of any heating system in the flats had led to some tenants being forced to use paraffin heaters or portable gas heaters, with a corresponding increase in moisture generation. The chosen solution to the walls was to provide a new weatherskin of 50mm insulation with a self-coloured rendered finish. The insulation is of a type containing chlorofluorocarbons, but it was specified before detailed information on the composition of insulation materials had been published. There is no reason why, in future schemes, a non-CFC material could not be used.

The render incorporates movement joints at each floor and vertically to break it into small panels to reduce the risk of cracking. The new skin copes with the rain penetration, but it would allow cold bridging to occur at the gables in top floor flats, from the heated room, through the cavity in the blocks, to the cold roof void. The concrete slabs forming the balconies to each flat were also a cold bridge. The solution to the gable cold bridge was cheap and effective, and made a benefit out of the Wilson block construction. With a new outer skin, it was a simple matter to fill the 100mm cavity in the blocks with blown-in mineral fibre. This reduced the U-value from $2 \cdot 43 W/m^2K$ to $0 \cdot 25 W/m^2K$, with the additional cost of the cavity fill being small compared with the external insulation necessary to counter the rain penetration [9].

The cold bridge to the loft is now only through the inner leaf of the block where it passes from the warm room into the cold roof space. The filling of the cavity in the Wilson blocks turns the perceived disadvantage of the apparently unsatisfactory construction into a positive advantage, by giving insulation levels far higher than could be achieved by the cladding and filling of a conventional brick cavity wall. The new external finish also provides a clear sense that the flats have been improved – it is a visible sign of change.

Each flat also has a wall to the common stair, and on each floor one flat has a wall separating the second bedroom from a shared store in the stairwell. The walls to the staircase, even in Wilson block buildings, are of brick cavity construction, but the store wall is of single skin brick. The chosen solution was to cavity fill where possible, and provide an insulated dry lining to the wall of the store. The end result is that almost all cold bridges are eliminated, and any remaining can be controlled by judicious siting and sizing of the heating system.

The roof insulation thickness was upgraded to 200mm and improved ventilation of the roof void was also provided. The U-value through the ceiling was reduced to $0.2W/m^2K$.

The lowest flats had their ground floors insulated with mineral fibre fixed between the joists to bring the insulation level in line with that of the roof (approx 150mm insulation thickness).

Existing single-glazed steel-framed windows were rusty, draughty and a cause of considerable heat loss. The frames lacked any thermal barrier and were a constant focus of condensation. All windows were replaced with upvc frames carrying double glazing units with a 20mm gap between panes. It could be argued that upvc is not an 'ecological' material, but on the other hand the windows will not need maintenance from a hard-pressed local authority. When budgets are limited, it is commonsense to invest in components that need no routine maintenance from landlord or tenant.

(2) Heating

Heating was provided by means of both gas and electric systems. Both installations include a 'feature fire' in the living room to provide a focus to sit round. The use of electricity for space heating is not a very effective way of reducing CO_2 emissions, but the use of two different heating systems allowed comparisons to be made and resulted in the supply of much help in kind from the gas and electricity industries, which would not have been forthcoming if one fuel had been excluded from the heating proposals. These are the compromises that must be made to allow projects to proceed in a climate of minimum public expenditure. In the Easthall scheme, the overriding concern was to enable the residents to heat their flats at a reasonable cost.

In addition to the heating systems, the scheme makes use of passive solar energy techniques to provide additional heat in two ways. There are two passive elements: one is formed by glazing in the balcony that is outside the principal bedroom of each flat. The bedroom window is replaced by a sliding double-glazed door allowing the extension of the bedroom into the sunspace when the weather is suitable. The double-glazed sunspace provides heating by acting as a solar-warmed buffer to the bedroom and adjoining living room, but it also acts as a source of solar pre-heated ventilation air to these rooms, which can draw their air supply through it. The glazing of the balconies also eliminates the cold bridge of the concrete balcony floor slab.

A second sunspace is created by a highly glazed extension forming a utility room/conservatory behind the kitchen. This buffers the kitchen and bathroom by covering the existing walls and windows, and provides extra space in the kitchen, allowing the washing machine and drier, both major sources of moisture generation, to be removed from the inside of the flat. The conservatory is built of upvc framing similar to that used for the windows, and is double glazed. Studies have shown that buffer spaces of this type are particularly valuable compared with direct gain passive solar solutions in northerly latitudes [10, 11, 12, 13]. The temperature of the buffer is related to solar gain in spring and autumn, while in winter it is largely a function of heat loss from the dwelling into the buffer [14]. Even a north-facing buffer space will benefit from the effect of raised temperature due to house heat loss and will therefore be able to supply pre-warmed ventilation air.

(3) Ventilation

Ventilation air is taken wherever possible from the buffer spaces to overcome the heat loss caused by bringing in air at outside temperature. In addition, simple mechanical passive ventilators are installed in kitchen and bathroom, the 'wet' areas, to create additional ventilation flow when humidity levels require it. The ventilators incorporate small rubber bladders which expand when dry and shrink when wet, so opening or closing the ventilation opening into the rising ductwork. Airflow is induced by fans in the roofspace, one for a set of three kitchens and one for a set of three bathrooms.

The bathroom window is sealed, so as to ensure that ventilation air enters the bathroom from the rest of the flat, reducing the chance of moist air escaping back into it. This intelligent ventilation is hence more economic than more common fan-assisted methods. The high levels of insulation mean that tenants can afford to heat their flats, and so paraffin stoves and other sources of unwanted moisture are eliminated, reducing the overall moisture vapour burden.

(4) Drying

In the Easterhouse flats a major source of moisture vapour is the drying of clothes. A drying area is provided at ground level in the 'back court' or communal garden, but because of the risk of theft most tenants choose to use tumble-driers, or to dry clothes in front of the fire. Driers are usually vented directly into the kitchen in winter, as it is too cold to put the outlet hose through an open window. In either case the water given off by the clothes passes directly into the flat to condense on the cold walls and single glazing, causing all the usual miseries of mould growth, damage to clothes and furnishings, and health problems.

The provision of the utility/conservatory space provides somewhere to dry clothes that is outside the flat but under the individual tenant's control. The solid panels in the conservatory walls under the glazing are even provided with knock-out vents to which the extract hose of a tumble-drier can be connected to ensure that vapour passes to the outside air. Unlike a conventional heating system, the sunspaces have functions that go well beyond the simple provision of heat. They increase the area of the flat and help to reduce the threat of condensation.

(5) Costs

As described above, the new sunspaces provide valuable internal amenity space, but their external impact is also considerable. Together with the external insulation with its new render finish, they are a visible sign that the block of flats has been remodelled, giving a new image to the hated Wilson block construction. If tenants can see the actual benefits, they will be more prepared to put up with all the disruption of being decanted while the work is being carried out.
An energy audit carried out by Heatwise in Easterhouse [15] supported earlier

findings of TSA [16, 17]. In a typical two-bedroom flat, similar to those used for the first rehabilitation project, the cost to provide heating 'to a reasonable standard' would be between £25 and £40 per week averaged over the year. A similar flat built to the standards of the 1982 Building Regulations would show a saving of 59–69% depending on its position in the block. In an area of poverty and high unemployment some households were spending over £1,000 per year (1988 prices) on fuel in an attempt to keep warm.

The study showed that Easterhouse residents were spending more than the national average on fuel although they lived in small flats only 60m² in area. They were spending more on fuel than the 'notional fuel element' allowed for by the DHSS in calculating welfare benefit rates. Many tenants were in the position of owing money to the fuel suppliers and were having sums deducted weekly from their benefits to pay for these arrears, reducing still further the amount they could spend on heat.

The result of all this was that most people could not heat their flats and some were reduced to heating one room. The Wilson block construction combined poor insulation with minimal heat retention; with a 2kW electric fire it took four hours to heat a living room from 13 to 21°C when the outside temperature was a few degrees above zero. When the fire was turned off the living room temperature fell back to 13° in only an hour. The rest of the flat was unheated over the week of the study, and the children's bedroom never reached a temperature higher than 10°C, while the outside temperature varied from 9 to minus 3°C. The cost to that household to provide this minimal degree of heat was £6, a sum which the Department of Energy estimated would 'heat comfortably' the whole of the flat [18].

Following the adoption of the Heatfest measures, at a cost of about £30,000 per flat (considerably less than the cost of demolition and rebuilding), the heating loads have been reduced by about 80%. Space heating costs (excluding hot water, cooking, lights and appliances) have been reduced from a theoretical £20 per week for a two-bedroom flat to an actual £3 per week [19].

The benefits

Many thermal upgrading schemes show little actual cost saving because residents choose to carry on spending what they spent before, but after the upgrading they can enjoy higher temperatures. In the Easthall scheme, tenants spend less and enjoy the comfort of full central heating throughout the flat. There are also benefits for the local authority who own the flats; they are easy to rent after they have been upgraded, and they do not deteriorate due to condensation, so reducing maintenance costs and prolonging the life of the housing stock. The local economy benefits from money being spent on goods and services rather than on high fuel bills. Local health is improved by the elimination of damp, condensation and mould. Lastly, the thermal upgrading reduces the emissions of carbon dioxide that are related to the servicing of buildings.

The Easterhouse project shows what can be achieved by an alliance between tenants and professionals. It also makes very clear the amount of commitment needed to bring about change. The Easthall Residents Association assisted in the formation of the Easterhouse Anti-Dampness Campaign in 1982. By 1990 they had got a single block prototype, six flats converted out of a total of 15,000, and have since successfully submitted a bid to the European Community for a demonstration project to upgrade a further thirty-six flats.

The Easthall thermal upgrading scheme was set up by the tenants; the architects and academics provided the information that they needed to enable them to see the refurbishment through to a successful conclusion. There was no agonising over whether the detailing should be High-Tech or Classical, the final form of the building is a straightforward expression of what was done to it. The architectural concerns were to do with cost and technical performance. It is satisfying to be able to point to a scheme where members of the architectural profession have made such a valuable contribution to user satisfaction combined with the serious addressing of green issues.

Clients: Easthall Residents Association
Architects: Community Architecture Scotland (coordinator, S. Howieson)
Energy advice: Mackintosh School of Architecture (Colin Porteous)
Contractor: Arthur

References

(1) Scottish Office Building Directorate (1987), *A guide to non-traditional and temporary housing in Scotland 1923–1955*, HMSO Edinburgh.

(2) TSA (1985), Technical Services Agency, Easthall Residents Association, *Thermal/dampness fabric survey*, 1985.

(3) TSA (1986), Technical Services Agency, Easthall Residents Association, *1985/86 Monitoring appraisal*, 1986.

(4) Porteous C. (1988), 'Heatfest – community architecture route to solar refit', *Sun at work in Europe No. 6*, October 1988. Technical Services Agency (TSA), Glasgow. *Town Planning Review*, Vol. 59 No. 1, January 1988, Liverpool University Press.

(5) Fielding M. (undated), *Heatfest*, Mackintosh School of Architecture, University of Glasgow.

(6) Heatwise (undated), *Heatwise Glasgow Information Pack*, Heatwise, Glasgow.

(7) Heatwise (undated), *Heatwise Glasgow: an ERA of partnership*, Heatwise, Glasgow.

(8) Easthall Residents Association (1990), *Demonstration Project No. SE167/88/UK ERA*, Glasgow.

(9) *Ibid.*

(10) Bartholomew D. (1985), 'Possibilities for passive solar house design in Scotland', *Ambient Energy* Vol. 6 No. 3, July 1985, pp147–158.

(11) Baker N. (1985), 'The thermal design of conservatories for solar ventilation preheating', *Procs. C39 Greenhouses and Conservatories: aspects of thermal behaviour and energy efficiency*, pp1–13, UK-ISES.

(12) James R. and Dalrymple G. (1985), 'Modelling of conservatory performance', *Procs. C39 Greenhouses and Conservatories: aspects of thermal behaviour and energy efficiency*, pp14–24, UK-ISES.

(13) Porteous C. (1985), 'The potential for sunspace buffer zones in Scottish housing', *Ambient Energy* Vol. 6 No. 3, pp137–146, July 1985.

(14) ERA (1990), *op. cit.*

(15) Sheldrick W. (1988), *Heating costs in Easterhouse: an energy audit and fuel cost survey*, Heatwise, Glasgow.

(16) TSA (1985), *op. cit.*

(17) TSA (1986), *op. cit.*

(18) Sheldrick (1988), *op.cit.*

(19) ERA (1990), *op. cit.*

Spectrum 7 Office/Industrial Building, Milton Keynes

Milton Keynes in Buckinghamshire has a long track record in low-energy design. It was here that a 40m² solar collector was added to one of the standard local authority houses in the early 1970s to investigate the potential of solar space and water heating. Later, the Homeworld exhibition provided a built demonstration of some of the possibilities of domestic energy efficiency. This exhibition was followed by Energy World, which again invited architects and developers to construct a series of energy-saving houses for sale after the exhibition.

However, part of the Energy World package was the establishment by the Milton Keynes Development Corporation (MKDC) of the Energy Park, an area of the new city where energy-efficient techniques of site planning and building design would be demonstrated. Through the 1980s, when energy tended to disappear from architects' perceptions in the pursuit of other goals, Milton Keynes Development Corporation continued with their belief in the essential importance of energy-efficient design.

Milton Keynes Energy Park was promoted by the Development Corporation as 'an international demonstration project to promote energy efficiency' [1]. The total project, occupying a site to the south-west of the city centre, will incorporate 1,200 houses, commercial developments and community facilities. The Park is intended to promote energy efficiency, but also to provide an attractive environment for home and work, and to provide investment opportunities. In addition to MKDC's normal development criteria, the Energy Park has special energy policies. These are designed to minimise energy demand in three ways: by orienting roads and development sites so as to maximise the possible solar gains; by modifying the microclimate around each site by the use of planting and shelter belts; and by setting performance targets for the energy consumption of the buildings within the Park.

Thirty hectares of the Energy Park have been earmarked for commercial development, with space for about fifty companies. Housing developments in the Energy Park must be designed in conjunction with the Milton Keynes Energy Cost Index, a computer program based on the Building Research Establishment's BREDEM model. The Index provides a simple method for predicting the energy performance of a house, and produces a single guide number to allow one design to be compared with another. It is similar to the official fuel consumption figures published for cars. A similar but more complex technique is used for industrial and commercial buildings.

The competition design

A limited competition was held for the first commercial developments in the Park in 1987. Entrants were asked to submit designs for a commercial/industrial building suitable for 'high-tech' companies. An energy brief was given based on the energy targets of the Chartered Institute of Building Services Engineers' Energy Code 2a. Since the MK commercial energy code had not been finalised at the time of the competition, the target given was the CIBSE code less 40 percent.

The competition was won by a team comprising ECD Partnership as architects, and Ove Arup & Partners as structural, mechanical and electrical engineers.

The north elevation and entrance canopy

(photograph: ECD Partnership)

Both parties acted jointly as energy consultants. Both practices have a long interest in low-energy design, although ironically ECD were forced to change their name from Energy Conscious Design in the 1980s because of the lack of interest in energy matters among clients and other architects at that time.

The designers entered the competition with developers Bride Hall, who set precise commercial requirements for the building on top of the energy targets of the MKDC brief. The building had to be lettable, so it could not cost more than a normal building in what is now known as the B1 category of mixed commercial/industrial uses. It had to have flexibility built in so that a tenant could convert it into production space, offices, research and development or any combination, with no sense that it was in any way compromised. Part of these normal commercial requirements for this type of space is the incorporation of a cooling system. Developers say that tenants expect this in a high quality building, and the designers had to provide it. Car parking spaces were also to be provided at normal levels.

It is easy to criticise a building for appearing to be energy-efficient and then being set in a vast car park. In fact, Milton Keynes is one of the few UK cities that has, like the earlier new town, Stevenage, a proper network of cycle ways, so access to the building by bicycle is relatively straightforward. The layout of the Energy Park also means that the development is within walking distance of housing areas, so there is at least the potential for a more efficient journey to work for the occupants.

The designers' starting point was the realisation that a building in the commercial/light industrial sector typically uses more energy for lighting and cooling than for heating. If they were to meet the energy target set by MKDC they would have to rethink the provision of these two services. This led them to a single-storey solution with high levels of daylighting. The Development Corporation stipulated the area of development versus open space on the site, and this was fortunately sufficient to allow a single-storey solution which simplified the provision of adequate daylight through roof glazing with north-facing saw-tooth pattern rooflights. The adoption of this traditional daylighting solution and its obvious reference to the factories of the past makes the point that this is an industrial building.

The other key design decision was the determination to avoid the use of air-conditioning to provide the cooling required by the developer. This was seen as an essential part of the low energy strategy. High daylighting levels would reduce the heat gain from electric lights and this would permit the use of cooling that would not need to employ refrigeration.

In a conventional daylit building of more than one storey (perhaps with production space on the ground floor and offices above) ventilation is provided by opening windows on the windward side to admit air, and on the leeward side to allow it to escape. As it passes across the building, the air picks up heat from people, lights and office machinery, and its temperature rises. The farther the air has to travel, the more heat it gains, and this puts a limit on the overall width of the building. As the building width increases, the distance of the central areas from the glazed perimeter also rises, increasing the use of electric light and adding to the heat load.

The usual limit of building depth beyond which air-conditioning is assumed to be needed to control the rise in ventilation air temperature is between 12 and 15m [2]. The Spectrum 7 building is about 60m² on plan.

Lighting from the roof

In a deep plan building the major elements are the roof and the floor; at Spectrum 7 the roof and floor are each over 40% of the total surface area and the walls are only 12%. The role of the roof, in addition to keeping the interior dry, is threefold: to admit daylight, to exclude sunlight, and to keep in the heat in winter. This may sound perverse, because most people would assume that solar gains should be admitted rather than excluded, but in a commercial or industrial building the problem of summer cooling is often much greater than that of winter heating because of the gains from lights and equipment. The Spectrum building was designed to face north, with the south elevation completely solid to exclude the sun, and the east and west elevations partially glazed. Only the north-facing side is fully glazed to admit the maximum amount of daylight, using low-E coated double glazing to give a U-value of 1·9 W/m²K.

The north-facing roof glazing was designed using both the enormous computing resources of Ove Arup & Partners, and large scale models tested in the artificial sky at University College, London. The design of the roof trusses was optimised to give the best balance of lighting versus heat loss through the glazing, which is clear double glass to maximise light transmission. The rooflights do not in fact face due north because of the layout of the site, and the glazing bars have substantial upstands to shield the glass from low-angle sun. The roof also overhangs the top of the glazing to give additional solar

The daylit interior

(photograph: ECD Partnership)

protection. There is a certain amount of sun penetration in the early morning, but this is not a problem. The architects looked at the possibility of arranging the rooflights diagonally, so as to face due north, but this would have introduced an off-grid alignment, thereby creating impossible problems for tenants trying to fit out the space, and so the compromise solution was adopted.

The roof design determined the structure, because the column grid of 8·8m in one direction is set by the design of the trusses which in turn were the result of the daylight optimisation studies. In the other direction the column grid is 12m, and there is a planning grid of 1,200mm for glazing bars, ceiling tiles and similar items. The structure is a simple steel frame with steel trusses at 6m centres. The trusses carry the glazing and are extended to support wide insulated gutters at the base of each run of northlights. The gutters are wide enough to walk along for maintenance and glass cleaning, and have downpipes only at the ends. The roof covering is profiled steel with a white PVF2 finish to reflect solar radiation and so help prevent overheating. Steel undertrays provide a ceiling finish and support a vapour barrier, with spacers to carry the outer sheet and 150mm glass fibre insulation.

The building was designed initially to be half office and half production area, and the exposed trusses in the office part have a suspended ceiling fixed to the lower horizontal member. This flat soffit then breaks back at the rooflights to create a triangular lighting zone. The artificial sky studies were used to determine the colour and profile of the ceiling for best lighting quality and quantity. They also showed that the roof colour had little influence on the light within the building. The model, made of cardboard at 1:10 scale, was designed to be easily modified and adapted so that different forms and finishes could be tried. The model gave the designers a chance to measure lighting levels and compare them with the computer predictions (there was a close correlation), but it also provided a clear understanding of the quality of the light in the space. The light levels within the building are unexpectedly high for a deep plan, and a source of satisfaction for designers and users alike, with a value achieved throughout the building of 900 lux even in December [3].

The roof profile and ducting

(photograph: ECD Partnership)

Electric lighting is of course provided, with surface-mounted fluorescent fittings on ceiling tracks for maximum flexibility in fitting out, as tenants can move them as required. Sensors which measure lighting levels inside and outside are combined with a microprocessor which turns on the lights in groups according to the conditions, avoiding the unnecessary use of electricity but supplementing the daylight as needed. It is calculated that the energy saving produced by the daylighting and the lighting control system amounts to a reduction of 70 percent [4].

Heating and ventilation

The roof also serves to distribute the heating and ventilation. In a deep plan building mechanical ventilation is essential, and it therefore seems a logical move to incorporate heating into the same system. In summer, 20% of the northlights can be opened as required by means of remote operators fixed to the columns to provide additional ventilation. A northlight roof is well suited to the distribution of services in one direction, as there are useful voids in the trusses between the northlights. In the other direction, service runs are complicated by the need to be able to place partitions anywhere within the space, uninterrupted by ducts running below the ceiling.

The solution at Spectrum 7 was to run the heating and ventilating ducts externally, and these ducts, insulated in their spiral-wound steel covers and powder-coated bright blue, give the building much of its architectural character. The ducts run along the east and west sides of the building and connect into two free-standing curved blocks that incorporate the plant and the sanitary accommodation, leaving the entire area of the building as a single flexible space. It is a similar approach to that used by Richard Rogers at Lloyd's. There are two ducts each side, supply and extract, and they are mounted side by side. The ends of the roofs extend over the ducts, from which simple connections run up into the roof spaces to join the supply and extract ducts that hang from the trusses and run from one side of the roof to the other. In the building adjustable registers attached to the ducts distribute the air from the ceiling.

Heating is provided by gas-fired modular boilers, and the amount of fresh air admitted to the system in winter is controlled by carbon dioxide sensors which respond to the exhalations of the occupants. The heating load is reduced by bringing in cold fresh air only when it is needed, with the heat taken out of the space by the extract ducting being recirculated where possible. The whole heating and ventilating system is conventional for this type of building.

The two free-standing plant pods, on the east and west sides of the building, contain wcs at ground level, with a 100kW gas-fired modular boiler in a semi-circular glass-fronted plant room at the end. Above the boiler room is a semi-circular cold water storage tank, without insulation, but prevented from freezing by the boiler flue passing through it. The air-handling plant above the wcs is in a three-layer arrangement, with the machinery itself at the top and sound attenuators in the middle. The lowest section contains all the crossover connections to the ductwork, meaning that the visible part consists of four simple horizontal tubes emerging from the plant unit and connecting straight into the main ducts. This offers a neat visual solution. The siting of the plant in external pods made installation straightforward and gives excellent access for maintenance and replacement. The cost breakdown shows services to have been just over 29% of the total figure.

The cool floor

The other major surface in the building is its floor. If the function of the roof is to provide light, the function of the floor is to provide cooling. The initial approach was to try to link the floor with the heating and ventilating system, but it proved impossible to make enough area for heat transfer by casting air ducts into the slab, and the necessary fans would have used a lot of electricity. The solution adopted was to have an evaporative cooling tower outside the building and to pump cooled water at 18°C through polythene pipes buried in the concrete floor. The system is usually used for heating, and employs in this case about 16km of pipe. The cooling works at night using off-peak electricity to reduce costs and, because it is based on simple evaporation, requires no refrigeration system and therefore no CFCs. The evaporative cooling uses the night-time air temperature to cool the water

The graph shows how the internal temperature is reduced in hot weather by the use of the cooled slab, which lowers the air temperature by more than two degrees over the working day.

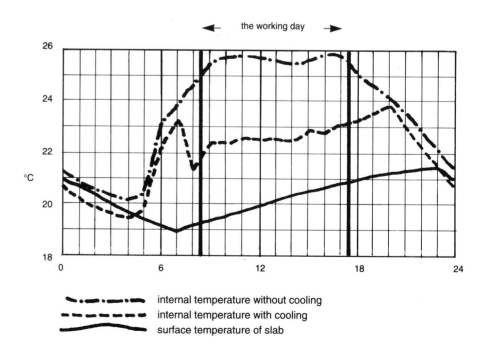

internal temperature without cooling
internal temperature with cooling
surface temperature of slab

passed through the slab, so that during the day the cool slab can absorb heat gains from within the building. The cooling tower is a standard manufacturer's model, enclosed within a steel casing, and sited near the front of the building in a small decorative pond.

In the office area there is a raised floor to allow computer and communications cabling to be distributed. The floor void is 600mm deep, so there is room to crawl around to make modifications, and also room for fan units that blow air out of registers in the floor. The floor void acts as a plenum with inlets from the space above to allow air to enter and be cooled by the cold slab. The surface of the concrete has an anti-dust finish painted on to prevent problems caused by its use for air distribution. The additional cost of increasing the void to 600mm compared with the more usual 150mm was very low, and allows tenants to make modifications without having to take up the carpets and floor panels.

The overall ceiling height in the building is 4m, slightly low for a factory, but high for an office. This allows the large floor void to be created for easy access and gives a sense of space in the office areas that is again unusual in a deep plan building. The production spaces do not have the raised floor and fan units, and are cooled by the slab directly. The slab provides about 4 degrees of cooling to the space on a typical summer day, keeping the temperature between 22 and 23°C.

The floor is constructed as a simple concrete slab with a power float finish. The large area of the building means that the floor is not insulated. Floor heat loss depends on the dimensions of the floor since it takes place at the perimeter where the heated space is adjacent to the cold exterior. In a slab the size of that at Spectrum 7 the ground beneath acts as an additional reservoir of (in this case) coolness. During the winter the slab cooling system is turned off.

The building was built with a perimeter edge beam which allowed the contractor to erect the frame and the weatherproof envelope, and then lay the slab 'indoors'. The cooling pipes are cast into the slab in individual 120m loops, running out and back from manifolds situated along the northern elevation. The manifolds are fixed above floor level, allowing any pipe loops that suffer damage to be turned off without affecting the operation of the remainder of the system. Great care was taken during the floor laying process to avoid damage to the pipes, with each pipe loop kept under air pressure during the pouring of the concrete. The result was that only one loop of 120m was lost out of the total installation. The U-value of the floor, based on the tables in the 1990 Building Regulations, is 0·15 W/m²K [5].

The external walls

The walls of the building vary according to their orientation as part of the solar exclusion strategy. On the southerly side, the roof is turned over the eaves and used as a wall, with one small window only. This side is close to the boundary where trees and bushes provide additional sun screening. The steel cladding is here backed up with a blockwork wall to provide the necessary fire resistance. On the east and west sides the walls are of foam-filled steel composite panels, with a U-value of 0·25 W/m²K. They have a silver PVF2 finish externally, and the steel inner lining provides the wall finish in the space. Panels can be unbolted and changed round by the tenant to relocate

The southerly side and boundary

(photograph: Robert Vale)

Architecture and 'green' concerns

door and window openings. A reasonable amount of glazing is provided in these walls.

Architecturally the building is extremely expressive of what it is doing. The plant rooms are visible, with boilers on display through their glass walls. The air handling units are painted the same blue as the ducts, making a clear statement of what is happening, and the ducts can be seen running from the units, along the walls and connecting up into the roof spaces. The perimeter glazing responds to solar conditions and daylight requirements. Finally there is the roof with its traditional northlights. At its ends the northlights are glazed in equilateral triangles, reflecting the line adopted by the ceiling where this is used internally. This is Modernism with an ecological face.

Inside, the spaces are bright and airy, helped by the unusually high ceiling of the offices. The reception, approached through a tunnel from the entrance, is glass-roofed, breaking the solidity of the profiled sheet and allowing some sunlight into the heart of the space like a small atrium. This glazed reception area is the only interruption to the space of the building.

The 'green' aspects of the design lie largely in its energy performance. The architects would like to know much more about the energy and environmental implications of the materials that they have used; the steel structure and cladding for example are in some ways energy-intensive, but how do they compare with alternatives? A simple calculation, based on the limited published data [6, 7, 8, 9] suggests that a steel-faced composite insulated panel has roughly half the energy content of a brick and blockwork cavity wall insulated to the same standard. However, this calculation excludes the energy aspects of the paint finish and jointing system for the panel, and does not take into account its design life. If a steel composite panel lasts thirty years and an insulated masonry wall lasts sixty, their energy use is the same on a time basis. The brick wall is also a structural element, whereas the panel wall relies on a separate frame for support.

The solution is to carry out detailed energy analysis on a number of different schemes for a given brief, to ascertain the kinds of construction that seem to involve the least energy use for a given building type. A necessary refinement of the technique will then be to calculate not energy usage but CO_2 emissions for materials processing and hence for building construction.

One aspect of the building that the designers would seek to avoid in a future building is the use of CFC-blown insulation in the cladding panels of the walls, but at the time of the design in January 1987 the data about the use of CFCs had not been published [10]. The largest area of the building, the roof, uses mineral fibre insulation rather than composite panels.

What makes the Spectrum 7 building so interesting is the way it challenges so many preconceptions on the part of both developers and architects. It was not built with the aid of grants or special funding; it was a straight commercial proposition by the developer, Bride Hall Developments, and the funding body, Postel Property Services, and it had to meet the strict commercial criteria of these unsentimental organisations, who were naturally anxious to build only what would show a reasonable profit. No doubt the track record of the ECD Partnership and the enormous resources and experience of Ove Arup & Partners helped to convince the clients that the unusual concept would work.

The construction was simple and straightforward, with no serious problems and a 34-week contract period. The simplicity of the services and the separation of plant rooms from the building envelope added to the ease of construction. The cost was slightly higher than the norm for this type of building [11] but the standards of performance and finish are high. The proof lies in the fact that the developer found no problem in letting the building (to an optical firm) and the in-built flexibility of the design has permitted fitting-out by the tenant without compromising the original concept in any way. The tenant has followed the line of the rooflights in adding suspended ceilings, and has taken advantage of the track mountings to reposition the electric lights as required.

The primary reason for Spectrum 7 being an energy-efficient building (setting aside the skills of its designers), is that the Milton Keynes Development Corporation decreed that it should be so. If a developer wanted to build in the Energy Park, they would have to meet the MKDC energy targets. Some might have argued that no developer would build there because of the onerous conditions, but Spectrum 7 shows that it is possible to make money out of buildings that save energy. In a political climate where market forces are often the sole criterion for action, this is an encouraging discovery.

Client: Bride Hall Developments
Architects and energy consultants: ECD Partnership (partner in charge, Richard Ferraro; project associate, Tony Lucas)
Structural, mechanical and electrical engineers and energy consultants: Ove Arup & Partners (partner in charge, John Berry)
Main contractor: Lovell Construction (Northern)

References

(1) Anthony Williams & Partners (1988), 'Building dossier: Spectrum 7', *Building*, 28 October 1988.

(2) Berry J. and Ferraro R. (1989), 'Low energy for industry: Spectrum 7 at Milton Keynes', *Architects' Journal*, 17 May 1989.

(3) Ashley S. (1989), 'Factory finesse', *Building Services: the CIBSE Journal*, February 1989.

(4) Berry and Ferraro (1989), *op. cit.*

(5) Her Majesty's Stationery Office (1990), *The Building Regulations 1985 Approved Document L1 Conservation of fuel and power*, 1990 edition, HMSO, London.

(6) Szokolay S. (1980), *Environmental Science Handbook*, Construction Press Ltd., Lancaster.

(7) Tutt P. and Adler D. (eds) (1979), *New metric handbook*, The Architectural Press, London.

(8) Martin D. (ed.) (1983), *Specification 84*, The Architectural Press, London.

(9) Thermalite Limited (1985), *The handbook, Thermalite Limited,* Coleshill, Birmingham.

(10) Curwell S., Fox R. and March C. (1988), *Use of CFCs in buildings*, Fernsheer Ltd., London.

(11) Anthony Williams & Partners (1988), *op. cit.*

Two Mile Ash Houses,
Milton Keynes

In 1980, researchers at the Polytechnic of Central London (PCL) determined to investigate the construction of houses that made use of superinsulation technology to save energy. Superinsulation is the term used to describe a building which can meet the majority of its space heating demand from 'casual' heat gains, such as the heat emitted by the occupants, heat from appliances such as cookers, refrigerators and televisions, and heat from lights. Typical values for these heat gains range from 70W for an adult male when sleeping and 115W when seated at rest, to 352W for someone carrying out heavy work over an eight-hour period [1]. Szokolay (1980) gives the following figures for gains from various activities in a typical UK house:

- cooking 2000 kWh/annum;
- lighting 500 kWh/annum;
- refrigerator 350 kWh/annum;
- other appliances 650 kWh/annum.

A house containing three adults for twelve hours per day will have a gain of 1,300 kWh/annum. This figure combined with those due to the use of appliances and services suggests that a house might have total heat gains due to the occupants and their activities of 4,800 kWh/annum (this figure excludes any gains that may accrue from the hot water system).

Superinsulation is widely used in Scandinavia, the US and Canada and has been incorporated in more than 150,000 houses built in these countries alone, the large majority being of timber frame construction. In North America some builders even offer to pay the residents' fuel bills if these exceed a specified figure [2].

Superinsulation combines low fabric U-values, using perhaps 200–300mm of mineral fibre insulation in walls and roof, together with underfloor insulation and well-insulated glazing, with airtight construction to reduce ventilation heat loss. Once the building has been made airtight, a controlled ventilation system is used to provide the air needed by the occupants, and this usually incorporates a heat recovery system to allow the heat from the outgoing stale air to preheat the incoming fresh air [3]. The key attributes of superinsulated buildings are:

- high levels of insulation in the fabric (including glazing);
- airtight construction;
- controlled ventilation systems.

To be considered superinsulated, a house in the south of the UK would need to have a U-value of 0·25 W/m²K for the walls, 0·15 W/m²K for the roof, and 0·30 W/m²K for the floor. Windows would need to be at least triple-glazed to give a U-value no greater than 2·0 W/m²K [4]. In other climates the definition of superinsulation might differ, with more insulation needed in a colder climate.

The essence of superinsulation as an approach to design is that it is a largely technical solution and has little effect on the traditional concerns of the architect, such as orientation, views, response to site and visual appearance. In this it differs considerably from the passive solar design approach, where orientation is of prime importance because of the need to capture solar radiation in the building. Passive solar design, with its emphasis on large areas of south-facing glazing, also has an inevitable impact on the building form and appearance.

In a passive building, the need for thermal mass to absorb the heat gains through the glazing predicates a heavy construction; a superinsulated building can be heavy or light as preferred. Generally, it is not easy to tell that a building is superinsulated by looking at it, whereas a passive solar scheme is usually self-evident. This description of the differences between the two approaches (referred to in North America as 'mass-and-glass' or 'light-and-tight') is not intended to imply that one is any better or worse than the other, only that they are different routes to the same goal. In fact, a passive solar building will need high levels of insulation if the solar gains are to make a useful contribution to space heating [5], just as the windows of a superinsulated building will admit solar radiation that will make a contribution to the space heating. (This effect will occur in any building that has windows that face the sun [6]).

Project design

The decision to build some superinsulated houses and by monitoring their performance determine what, if any, advantages they could offer in the UK, meant that as far as possible it was desirable to use construction methods that were well proven. It was the performance of superinsulation that was to be tested, not the technology itself. For this reason, the researchers at PCL chose to use an off-the-peg Scandinavian timber frame construction system because it was tried and tested. The use of a system that was already in production gave a guarantee both of the integrity of the insulation and of low air leakage.

In Scandinavia, Germany and North America there is far more use of prefabricated house construction systems than in the UK. This is probably due to the predominance of timber construction in these countries, which lends itself to the assembly of ready-made panels in a factory. The severe winters experienced in these countries may also be an influence, whereas the UK's temperate climate allows outdoor construction of masonry buildings all through the year. In Sweden, 70% of houses were factory-produced in 1984 [7].

The design process for the superinsulated houses lasted from the original proposal in 1980 to the start on site in 1985. Part of the time was taken up with an application that proved successful for funding from the European Community to pay for the monitoring that was an essential part of the project. The researchers contacted a number of importers of timber-framed superinsulated house kits, and finally settled on a firm called Finlandia, who imported houses from Finland. The importer also found a developer who was prepared to work with the research team. Support was forthcoming from Milton Keynes Development Corporation, who allocated a site for the houses in Two Mile Ash, an area just to the west of the centre of the new city. The site was 92m x 26m, with the long axis fronting on to a residential street running north–south, giving the front and back of the houses an east–west aspect.

The researchers were determined that the houses should not be over-large; they wanted houses of a conventional size to demonstrate that energy saving techniques were relevant to 'normal' houses. They decided to put twelve houses on the site, in six semi-detached pairs. The houses were to be built for sale, the selling agents advising that they should be of two storeys with three

Street elevation and garage
(photograph: Robert Vale)

bedrooms and a garage, while the developer fixed a floor area of 75m² for each house. The designers felt that this was rather small, and eventually persuaded the developer to add a reasonably generous hall on to the basic house.

The east–west orientation of the houses suited the project aims, because it minimised the effects of solar gains in the winter. This may sound perverse, but it enabled the effects of the superinsulated construction to be monitored without the need for the solar contribution to be measured and calculated and then subtracted from the final result. The twelve houses were divided into two groups: four houses were to be fully superinsulated, and the other eight were to be built in accordance with the Building Regulations current at the time, to act as a control. In fact, the control houses were built with more insulation than the Building Regulations minimum, because the selling agents felt that they would otherwise be hard to sell next to the superinsulated ones. At least as they were built, the agents could claim that they were better insulated than the norm – even the best-planned experiment has to defer to the rule of the market-place on occasion. The four superinsulated houses each cost about £2,000 more than the control houses, with the difference made up by the European Community funding.

The construction

The use of a ready-made timber frame system also had the advantage that the basic shells of the houses could be erected quickly. The panels were made in Finland by a firm called Oravais, with detailed design overseen by Finlandia Construction, the importers. The basic panels used 145mm-thick studs, plus 40mm-thick cross-battens on the inner face. The air-vapour barrier, which makes the construction airtight, was installed between the battens and the studs, forming a 40mm-wide zone in which pipes and wires could be run with no fear

The foundations use aerated concrete blocks to support the bottom plate of the timber frame, with under-slab insulation plus edge insulation to reduce the cold bridge.

The damp proof membrane under the floor laps with the vapour barrier in the wall, which is set in from the inner face of the room to form a zone in which pipes and wires can be distributed without puncturing the barrier.

A clear cavity is formed between the sheathing of the timber frame and the external brick cladding for maximum weather protection. The cavity is closed by a timber lining round the window frame, while a tiled cill and metal flashing seal the bottom edge.

On the first floor the brick cladding is replaced by painted fibre-cement boarding.

Conventional roof trusses are used. with a vapour barrier and wiring gap, and spacers keep an air path between the roof insulation and the sarking felt.

The position of the insulation under a cold attic necessitates a draught-sealed loft access hatch to avoid both air movement and vapour problems.

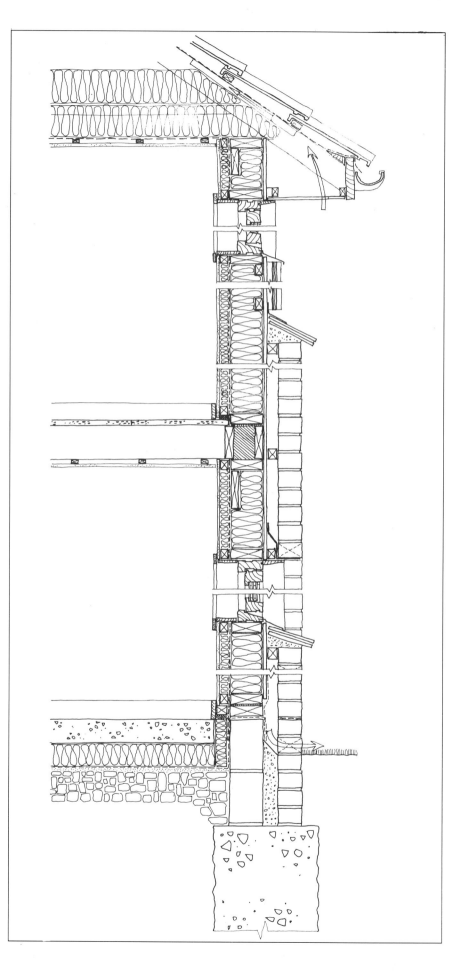

Typical constructional section

of damaging or puncturing the barrier. The outer face of the studs was covered with bitumen-impregnated fibreboard sheathing, and the inner finish was 12·5mm plasterboard. The ground floor had a brick external skin, with a cavity between it and the fibreboard, while the first floor, above the level of the window cills, was clad in painted mineral fibre board.

The wall panels arrived on site in a container 10m long and 2·4m high, allowing external wall panels to be the full width of the building, with joints needed only at the corners and at the junction between ground and first floor. This was an obvious benefit in achieving a high level of airtightness in the construction. The panels were delivered completely finished, with the air-vapour barrier, insulation, cladding both internal and external, electrical conduits and pre-glazed doors and windows already in place. Because they were made inside a heated factory, greater quality control was possible than could be achieved on a normal building site where work has to be carried out in the rain.

The standard windows offered by the Finnish manufacturer were triple-glazed; the designers had this specification upgraded on the superinsulated houses to include a pane of low-emissivity glass and argon filling to the cavities, giving an overall U-value of 1·2 W/m²K. The control houses were single-glazed. Window surrounds were filled with sprayed polyurethane foam (the problem of CFCs was not apparent at the time; non-CFC versions of this material are now available) to ensure that they were as airtight as possible. The trimmer joists at the first floor panel and floor junction were also filled with foam, and strips of air-vapour barrier were fixed to the edges of the floor panels to allow a continuous seal to be made with the walls when the floor panels were installed on site.

The ground floors of the houses were not prefabricated, and consisted in the superinsulated houses of a 100mm-thick concrete slab laid on top of 100mm of Styrofoam extruded polystyrene (containing CFCs). A 50mm-thick layer of Styrofoam was carried round the perimeter of the slab to try to avoid any cold bridging at this point, although the wall insulation above floor level is considerably greater in thickness than this strip of edge insulation. The use of insulation under the whole slab was chosen to isolate the slab completely from ground moisture which could act to remove heat, and isolation was further achieved by putting the insulation, which is water-resistant, on top of a damp-proof membrane on a blinded hardcore base. The insulated slab is the only large thermal mass in the houses; it was hoped that this would help to counteract summer overheating, which was also minimised by the avoidance of solar gains.

The roof

A roof of trussed rafters was used, with 300mm of glass fibre insulation. This was laid in three layers with the first fitted between the ceiling joists. Subsequent layers were then laid at right angles to the preceding one to minimise the effect of gaps. The result was a roof space in which there was no opportunity for storage because the timbers were completely buried in the insulation, but the designers were not concerned about this, since the trussed rafters were not designed to take the loads resulting from storage in the first place. Storage was provided in the garage roof, and in built-in cupboards.

Care was taken to design the eaves to allow ventilation of the roof void in such a way that it would not be blocked by the insulation. The insulation was kept away from the sarking felt so that any condensation that might occur could not

Rear elevation and garden wall

(photograph: Robert Vale)

run down the felt and into the dry insulation, with disastrous results. The access hatch from the house into the roof space was detailed to prevent the transfer of water vapour and to stop air movement. Extruded polystyrene 150mm-thick was glued to the hatch, which was fitted with EPDM rubber draught seals, and a deep surround was formed to retain the glass fibre roof insulation.

Heating

Both the superinsulated and the control houses used a novel type of heating system based on a thermal store situated between the boiler and the space heating and domestic hot water circuits. The principle is that the thermal store is kept at a constant temperature of 70–80°C by a small heat circulator, and allows the use of a smaller heat source because the store evens out peak demands. Domestic hot water is supplied at mains pressure by passing the water through two heat exchangers operating serially inside the heat store. They are positioned so that the domestic hot water supply takes heat from the bottom of the store, allowing heat stratification to continue to supply the space heating circuit from the top of the store. The system is similar to the more common 'combi-boiler' and allowed the designers to dispense with a cold water tank in the roof space, thus avoiding penetration of the air-vapour barrier in the first floor ceiling.

The heat store is designed for use with a simple gas-fired circulator with a rating of 3kW, but the available circulators were open-flued and would need a fresh air supply which would defeat the aim of producing an airtight building, so the designers opted for a room-sealed balanced flue gas boiler to heat the store with an output of 6kW. This was the smallest room-sealed appliance available that would meet the energy demand of the control houses. These have a conventional central heating system with radiators fed from the thermal store, but the superinsulated houses have a purpose-made water-to-air heat exchanger in the ductwork of the mechanical ventilation system.

The ventilation system and airtightness

The heat recovery mechanical ventilation system is made by Bahco of Sweden, and is based on a unit mounted in the kitchen which combines the fans, cross-flow heat exchanger, controls and filters in one unit which functions as a cooker hood. Thus it is conveniently placed to extract at source the water vapour from cooking activities, a major source of potential condensation. The location in the kitchen has at least two further advantages: the unit is accessible for cleaning the filters (essential in a cooker hood) and repairs, and it is not on the cold side of an air-vapour barrier, as it would be if it was in the loft. In that case it would need insulating, and the ducts running to and from the heat exchanger would have to be sealed to the barrier where they passed through it.

The size of the unit is such that it lines up more or less with standard wall cupboards, and the 100mm ducts from it run along above the top of the cupboards before crossing to the supply and extract points. The ducts are made of 100mm diameter spiral-wound galvanised steel, with a smooth internal surface which minimises air resistance. Bends are pre-formed and push into the straight sections with EPDM rubber gaskets for sealing. Air is extracted from the kitchen (by the cooker hood), from the bathroom, and from the ground floor wc. Supply is to the living room, dining room, the hall and the bedrooms, with distribution through the intermediate floor. This reduces the amount of ducting needed and, more important, avoids the need to puncture the air-vapour barrier in the first floor ceiling.

Airtightness in the superinsulated houses was achieved by careful detailing and by avoiding penetrations of the air-vapour barrier. The wall construction, with its 40mm service zone on the inside of the barrier, has already been described. The same technique was used on the first-floor ceiling, with all wires routed through a similar cavity. The design was slightly compromised by the need to put the heating system feed and expansion tank in the roofspace. This could have been avoided by putting the tank in the top of a cupboard or wardrobe or by using a pressurised system. The other large penetration was the soil vent pipe, which ran through the loft to a ridge terminal. The pipe was forced through the barrier, and then taped to it to make an airtight joint.

Penetrations of services through the walls were sealed with expanding polyurethane foam from a can, which was also used to ensure that all panel joints were airtight. The intake and output ducts of the ventilation system were similarly treated, but difficulties were encountered with the balanced flue of the boiler, which tore the barrier when inserted. Following pressure-testing of the houses, the flue terminal was sealed satisfactorily with mastic. The proof of the effectiveness of the sealing measures is that measurements made using the tracer gas sodium hexafluoride showed that the houses had a ventilation rate less than 0·1 air change per hour with the ventilation system turned off. This is very tight by normal standards. Similar results were obtained in a later pressurisation test.

Erecting the houses

The contractors had few problems with the erection of the houses, in spite of the rather novel (to the UK) techniques involved. The architects, Fielden Clegg of Bath (one of the few UK firms with a track record in low energy design), were employed by the developer to produce the design but, as is normal, not to carry out site inspections. Paul Ruyssevelt, an architect at PCL and one of the research team, acted as unofficial site architect, and the higher than average attention he was able to give the project helped to resolve problems before they

Lowering a prefabricated section

(photograph: Dr. Paul Ruyssevelt)

became serious. As the houses were for sale on the open market, they were also covered by the NHBC guarantee, and the NHBC inspector came once a week to oversee the work. The NHBC raised few queries regarding the unusual construction, which was not therefore an obstacle to the developer's ability to sell the houses.

The timber panel construction presented advantages and disadvantages. The basic shells went up in a day, with a 50m crane used to position the panels and finally to drop the complete roof onto the walls. The foreman's attitude was disparaging at the start, but at the end of the project he admitted that it had resulted in a cleaner site and easier management, adding that, if he ever did it again, considerable time savings could be made. Perhaps the biggest construction problem was using a 100mm-thick power-floated ground slab to avoid the need for a screed. The small area of each house meant that the power float tended to damage the exposed dpc at the edges of the slab, and much of the concrete had to be hand-floated.

There were the usual difficulties associated with the installation of unusual heating and ventilating equipment, often with instructions written in Swedish, and here the presence of the architect on site was of great value. Some difficulty was also experienced with the fitting of the roof insulation, particularly at the eaves, where 300mm thickness had to be pushed into an area where there was limited space and access. Thermographic surveys of the completed houses revealed where roof insulation was incorrectly placed, and this was then remedied.

On completion, the houses were sold on the open market, with a premium of £500 asked for the superinsulated ones over the control group. The superinsulated houses were bought first, suggesting that there may well be a market for houses that use advanced technology. Detailed monitoring of all the houses showed that the superinsulated houses used between £10 and £20 worth of gas (at 1986 prices) for space heating in a year, and showed an overall

Roof insulation in progress

(photograph: Dr. Paul Ruyssevelt)

saving on all energy of about £100 per year in comparison with the control houses. The superinsulated houses completely alter the balance of energy uses in the house, with space heating being the smallest component of the total consumption, and electricity for lights, appliances and the ventilation system the highest. Domestic hot water accounts for five to ten times more energy than space heating [8].

Experience in use

Paul Ruyssevelt lived in one of the houses with his family for more than a year, and found it very comfortable. He commented that it had a great sense of isolation from the outside weather, particularly in winter, and it was necessary to look at the monitoring system to see if the wind was blowing. This is mainly due to the absence of draughts, but the triple-glazed windows also provided acoustic as well as thermal insulation. Heating was used only during cold spells in January and February, with the heat recovery system left running for 24 hours a day during the winter. The heat exchanger in the ductwork was not large enough to give a rapid heat-up of the house after a long unoccupied period. When the temperature was below minus 1°C the heat exchanger was left running continuously, with the thermostat controlling the heat output as necessary. The heat recovery system proved to be reliable in operation and quiet enough to cause no disturbance.

The combination of very high levels of insulation in all external surfaces, plus high performance glazing, meant that room surfaces remained at temperatures very close to air temperature. The result of this was the virtual elimination of temperature gradients within the house, and an increase in the sensation of comfort. In the control houses, some surfaces such as the uninsulated ground floors and the single glazing were at temperatures considerably less than those of other surfaces, and were a source of thermal discomfort.

It may not seem surprising that one of the research team was satisfied with the superinsulated house, but the people who bought the other three houses also found them comfortable. The other occupants included a single nurse, and a family with three children. The occupants used the ventilation and heating systems in different ways, and by their presence provided differing levels of heat input from themselves and their activities. However, all felt that the superinsulated houses provided superior comfort conditions to those of a conventional house. They all also found no problem in coping with the unusual ventilation system.

The only disappointing aspect of the whole experiment was that the space heating and hot water systems proved less efficient than had been calculated, with larger than expected gas inputs needed to provide the necessary heat. This in no way invalidates the basic premise which was that superinsulation could offer greatly improved comfort while reducing energy demand compared with conventional construction.

Having achieved houses where the energy required for space heating is minimised, the next step must be to tackle the other areas of energy usage, particularly electricity, since this is the least efficient in primary energy terms when made from fossil fuels. Domestic hot water can be provided, at least partially, by solar energy, and low energy light fittings can be used. Manufacturers of domestic appliances in the UK must now follow the example of other countries and start to offer low energy refrigerators, freezers, cookers, washers and driers.

Clients: Coleman Homes
Architects: Feilden Clegg Design (partner in charge, Peter Clegg)
Contractor: Coleman Contractors
Monitoring: Polytechnic of Central London Research in Building Group
(Director, Professor John Littler; Researcher, Paul Ruyssevelt)

References

(1) Szokolay S. (1980), *Environmental Science Handbook*, the Construction Press Ltd., Lancaster, England.

(2) Olivier D. (1983), 'Energy efficient improvements and renewable energy sources: implementation in North America', Study Tour Report, *Earth Resources Research*, London, May 1983.

(3) Olivier D. (1986), 'Low energy masonry', *Building Services: the CIBSE Journal*, October 1986, pp37–38.

(4) Ruyssevelt P.A. (1987), 'Superinsulated houses for the UK', PhD thesis, Polytechnic of Central London.

(5) Everett R. (1980), 'Passive solar in Milton Keynes', *Research Report ERG031*, Energy Research Group, the Open University.

(6) Siviour J. (1977), 'Houses as passive solar collectors', *ECRC/M1070*, Electricity Council Research Centre, Capenhurst.

(7) Kando P. (1984), 'Made in Sweden: better houses come ashore', *Solar Age*, March 1984, pp24–28.

(8) Ruyssevelt P.A. (1987), *op. cit.*

The NMB Bank, Amsterdam .

In the UK, an organisation wanting a new office building usually rents it from a developer. The developer builds solely to make a profit, both from the rents and from the increased value of the plot once developed. The same system is used in the United States. Francis Duffy, writing in the *Architects' Journal*, makes the point that these modern office blocks are

'tradable commodities at worst and constructional feats at best. What they definitely are not is well worked out responses to the changing needs of modern organisations and modern office workers. Instead they represent a vision of office work (gangs of under-paid and under-privileged clerks) which is almost a century old.' [1]

These speculative offices on the North American pattern have some advantages, because their design is inherently adaptable to allow use in different ways by different organisations (although the adaptability is generally based on strictly orthogonal partitioning grids), and they tend to be economical in construction so as to maximise profit to the developer.

Where they tend to fall down, figuratively at least, is in the allocation of space. Because the driving force is maximum lettable space, the space that does not bring in rent is reduced to a minimum. This means that circulation areas, lift lobbies, stairs and wcs are made as small as possible because they are shared between users and not rented directly by them. The emphasis is on the lettable office space, and anything that cannot earn its keep is reduced to a minimum, with a consequent feeling of penny-pinching.

The public square at the entrance
(photograph: Alberts en van Huut)

Some of the towers and pentagonal
solar air heaters

(photograph: Alberts en van Huut)

The Anglo-Saxon model of office development is not the only way it can be
done. In some countries, a company wanting a new building arranges a bank
loan, approaches an architect or holds a competition, and builds itself premises
reflecting exactly what it wants and can afford. In Britain this process is seen
only occasionally, as in the Lloyd's building in London or, less successfully in
architectural terms, the Shell building on the South Bank.

There would seem to be considerable advantages to the firm in question in
building for itself. First, the cost must be less, since there is no intermediary to
take a profit from the deal; second, the increase in value of the site and the
building comes to the building owner; and third, the firm ends up with a
building designed specifically for its needs, and does not have to fit its
activities into an anonymous shell.

When the Nederlandsche Middenstandsbank (NMB), one of the three largest
banks in Holland, wanted a new head office in Amsterdam, they followed the
alternative route and built their own building. Being a bank, they had no
problems arranging the finance. They turned to the architectural practice of
Alberts en van Huut in Amsterdam for the design of the project. The architects
were chosen from an initial list of twenty possible practices. The Bank's own
development company advised on the choice, which was made by a committee
of Bank employees from a shortlist of three practices following visits to other
buildings they had designed. Alberts en van Huut were chosen because of their
human-centred approach to design, which they had demonstrated in housing
schemes and churches. They had never designed a large office block.

The initial design

The decision to build a new headquarters was taken in 1978; the Bank had
moved into a new building in 1974, designed to accommodate 1,200 people.
Rapid growth in the latter part of the 1970s meant that they had 2,500 head
office staff in five buildings scattered through Amsterdam and a neighbouring
town [2]. It was not possible to find a central city site in Amsterdam to build the
new building, and staff were consulted about the choice of a site in one of the
suburbs where new development was taking place, with a final choice made

Plan of first and ground floors

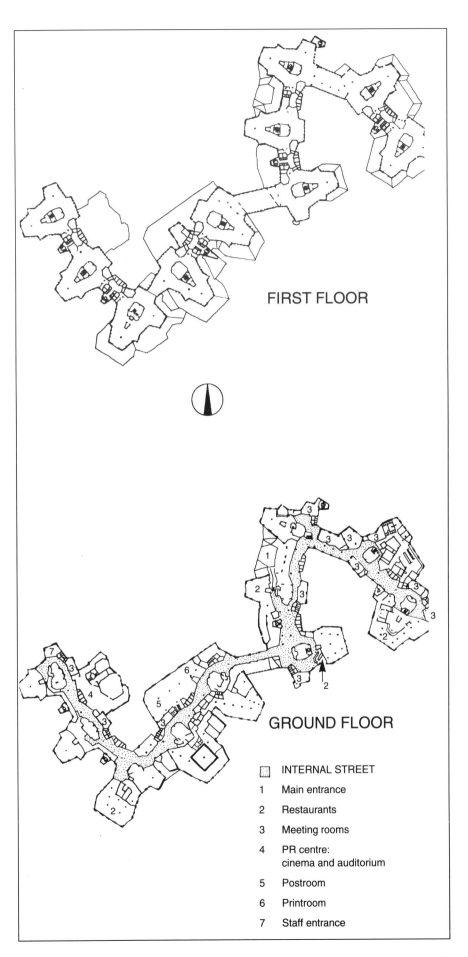

FIRST FLOOR

GROUND FLOOR

INTERNAL STREET
1   Main entrance
2   Restaurants
3   Meeting rooms
4   PR centre:
     cinema and auditorium
5   Postroom
6   Printroom
7   Staff entrance

between two locations. The chosen site is in the south-east, close to public transport (buses, underground and main line railway) as well as the road network. This site was preferred because a new shopping centre was being built there, which would give staff an opportunity to shop during the lunch break, as well as providing welcome variety from a purely office development.

The site offered to the Bank by the local authority was about 500m long, running alongside a dual carriageway road. The first design, to see if the requisite number of people could be accommmodated, was a simple block, 500m long, with offices both sides of a central corridor. However, the Bank wanted a building that would permit group working and encourage interaction betwen staff, and also one that would be energy-efficient. The energy consultants advised that the building should form a series of U-shaped courts to break the wind blowing across the flat landscape. This form would also reduce the impact of noise from the main road.

The design team then came up with a building which provided accommodation in a series of ten towers, linked by a route across the site. The T-shaped plan of each tower allowed group working as well as division into smaller units where necessary. The towers were splayed on plan to reflect the road noise more effectively. The Bank staff were worried that they would reflect the noise back on to adjoining buildings, so the towers were also splayed in section to send the noise upwards. The slope is only 4·5°, but it gives the building a profile unlike any other. The slope, which makes all the walls look like buttresses, also serves to give the visual impression of a building that is growing out of the earth. In the words of Ton Alberts, the architect, it is 'grounded to earth, open to the sun'.

The NMB Bank is built of brick cladding on a partly precast and partly in situ concrete structure (about 50:50). Walls have a 45mm cavity behind the brickwork, backed by 100mm mineral fibre insulation and the 180mm precast inner leaf. At first sight the most striking aspect is the sloping form of almost all external walls, and this continues through to the interior, where angled columns come down in unexpected places. Seen from a distance, surrounded by conventional office developments of the late 20th century, it looks like a cross between a mediaeval hill town and Kafka's castle.

The ten towers which make up the office accommodation are linked at ground level by a rambling internal street, varying in width and paved in marble. Off the street are conference rooms, a lecture theatre, a winter garden and a number of restaurants and eating places, which offer anything from a wholefood snack to an *haute cuisine* meal. The curving route on plan creates a series of spaces between the towers which have been landscaped as gardens, and most of the offices look on to these. The landscaping is lush and imaginative, and incorporates large areas of water, fountains and waterfalls. In different areas the gardens have differing characters, some formal and some wild. Under the gardens is a large basement car park whose fresh air inlets are hidden among the greenery above.

The office accommodation is in the towers, each containing a roughly T-shaped floor providing space for about 60 people. Where the arms of the Ts touch there are lifts, wcs and service spaces. In the centre of each T is an atrium void containing the stair that links it to the internal street at ground level. The result is first that all office space is within 7m of a window and, second, that the stairs, rather than the lifts, are the predominant means of circulation, giving more opportunity for people to meet, saving energy and providing exercise. The

Water flowing down one of the handrails

(photograph: Alberts en van Huut)

circulation at the centre of each tower also serves, via its glass roof, to bring light to the floor of the street, in addition to the light from the windows that provide views of the gardens as the street meanders across the site.

Each tower, while employing roughly similar forms and elements (for instance each contains the same prefabricated stair element), is different from the others in orientation, detailing and finishes. The central space of each is painted in pale pinks, blues or greens, and planting is provided on a lavish scale; in some it grows up the walls under daylight spectrum lamps, in others it is growing along wires crossing the void diagonally. The interior literally drips with plants.

The use of water

The interior also drips with water. Rainwater is collected from all surfaces, filtered through crushed shells, and pumped round the internal and external planting. Externally the waterfalls and fountains are enjoyable, and provide a sound that offsets the noise of city traffic for people having their meals outside one of the restaurants. Internally, the use of water is unusual and imaginative. There are water sculptures in many of the atrium spaces, and on one of the stairs a water handrail in precast bronze concrete elements, incorporating a series of weirs and splashes to aerate the water before it is pumped to the plants.

The use of water is part of the design philosophy to integrate the building with nature. The rainwater is collected and brought inside as a link with the natural environment, permeating the space with the sound of running water, but it is also a good way of watering the internal gardens. The shaping of the handrail is visually interesting, the shapes increase the sound made by the water, and the turbulence thus created helps to entrain oxygen in the water which increases its value to the plants.

User involvement in a healthy building

Providing a few plants and running water is often an architect's sole response to the 'greening' of a building. At the NMB Bank the greenness goes much deeper. At the more philosophical level the design team was, from the outset, non-hierarchical. Representatives of the client worked with the architect, the building physicist, structural and services engineers, acoustician, landscape consultants and interior designers [3]. The team was responsible for the whole building, and each member was encouraged to comment on the work of the others, avoiding the narrow specialisations that occur on so many projects.

Dutch legislation ensures that representatives of those who will work in a new building have an input to the design process, and the result is a much greater degree of user consultation than would be the norm in the UK or the United States. This gives a sense that the building belongs to those who work in it. Preliminary research by the Bank, based on data from its own health insurance scheme, would seem to confirm that health problems and absenteeism are lower than in a conventional building. The results of a full study will be issued soon.

As well as ensuring that the Bank's employees feel good about their building, the design team have tried to make the whole place healthy. They have attempted to avoid the problems of 'sick building syndrome' by maximising natural light and ventilation, and by giving a high degree of individual control to the users, a requirement that came from the consultations. The windows are designed to provide adequate light, about 500 lux during an average day, while excluding traffic noise and preventing excessive heat loss and unwanted gains.

About 20% of the wall area is glazed, with windows double-glazed in colour-coated thermally-broken aluminium frames. At the top of each is a glazed panel backed by reflective louvres which bounce light on to the white ceiling to increase the illumination at the back of the space. The rest of the window has

Inside one of the access towers
(photograph: Robert Vale)

The spacious marble-floored internal street is the principal means of circulation

(photograph: Alberts en van Huut)

motorised external blinds which operate when the temperature outside rises above 16°C (to reduce solar gain), combined with internal blinds that the users can adjust as required.

All the windows can be opened for ventilation. Electric lights adjacent to the windows are turned on automatically when daylight levels drop, and task lighting is provided at the desks to reduce the need for high overall light levels. This saves energy and gives visual contrast to the spaces. Users can switch lights on or off as required. The overall aim is to give as much control as possible at each workplace. However, in the public spaces the majority of the blinds had not been adjusted. When asked about this, the services engineers confirmed that the employees were not yet used to having that degree of control of their shared environment.

The artificial lights are all compact fluorescent lamps in a variety of fittings, some designed specifically by the services engineers. For instance, low energy downlighters fitted with Philips lamps provide background lighting to the internal street. The use of compact fluorescent lamps reduces internal heat gains within the building and provides the same illumination for less electricity, while avoiding the institutional appearance of conventional fluorescent tubes.

Heating and cooling

The whole building operates without conventional air-conditioning, as it is not sealed. At the top of each tower is a pentangular solar collector and a heat recovery unit. A variable proportion of the extracted air is recirculated back to the building, and the remainder passes across a heat wheel which extracts the heat from the exhaust air. Fresh air is brought in through the solar collector, which can raise its temperature by 22°C, and this air then receives further

The external wall consists of a precast concrete inner leaf 180mm thick, smooth enough to take a direct painted finish internally. This provides considerable thermal mass. In front of this is 100mm mineral fibre insulation . The insulation is faced with a breather membrane to exclude moisture.

The facing brickwork is designed to leave a clear cavity of 50mm between its rear face and the insulation. At the lintel this cavity is drained to the outside.

Cold bridging is avoided by the use of two separate lintels, the inner one integral with the precast concrete structure.

Insulated window linings and a thermally broken frame ensure that the insulation layer remains uninterrupted.

The box mounted on the transome contains the external sun blind. Above this is an area of clear glass with a silvered reflecting blind on the inside to bounce light to the ceiling from where it is reflected further back into the space.

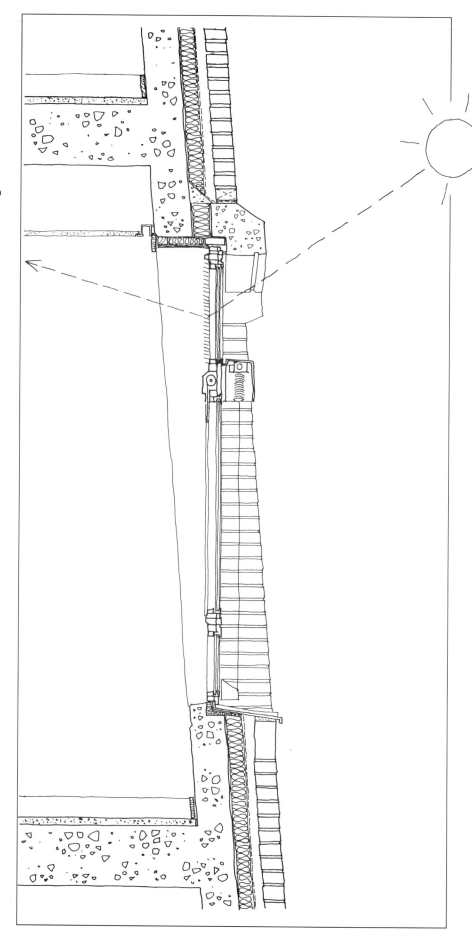

Typical section through
external wall

heating from the heat reclaimed from the exhaust air. The mixture of fresh and recirculated air is then heated if necessary by heater batteries. Heat comes from a central gas-fired boiler, but this is backed up by four 25,000 litre insulated water tanks which are used to store waste heat. The principal source of this waste heat is the building's electricity generators, which are powered by gas turbines. The system avoids the massive waste of heat that is the usual side-effect of centralised electricity generation. Heat is also reclaimed from the absorption refrigeration plant and from the lift machinery.

Although the building operates without air-conditioning, the quality of the internal air was an important consideration during the design process. The exposed areas of water within the building are used to provide a natural humidity to the air in the manner of the gardens and courtyards of the Alhambra, or the street fountains of Rome.

In summer the fresh air is drawn in direct from outside, and cooling batteries in the airstream, fed by absorption refrigeration units using some of the waste heat from the store, cool the air supplied to the building. However, the structure is deliberately thermally massive, containing about 40,000m^3 of concrete, and on summer nights the building is flushed with cool air to lower the temperature of the concrete ready for the day. The solar control blinds then help to control overheating and reduce the need for the refrigerating plant to operate. In winter this passive system works in reverse, with the heavy structure storing solar gains and gains from the users. When visited on a day with external temperatures in excess of 25°C, the building felt cool and comfortable.

Despite the alternative approach to servicing, the size and types of service run might be found in any modern office building, not least because of the massive use of office equipment within the bank, especially computers. The services duct follows the path of the main street in a lowered ceiling void and is thus readily accessible at all points within the building. Unlike many modern service ducts, that of the NMB Bank is clad in softwood.

The result of this combination of sophisticated control and simple passive systems is that the NMB Bank is, according to detailed measurements made by the Dutch Research Establishment (TNO), the most energy-efficient building in the world, with an overall primary consumption of 96kWh/m^2 per annum for an area of 48,600m^2. By comparison, the Bank's previous headquarters building, erected ten years earlier, had a consumption of 1,320kWh/m^2 per annum [3].

The Bank made a survey of the costs of new bank buildings in the Netherlands over the last ten years, and found that their new headquarters had cost 3 percent more to build than the ten year average figure. However, it saves them 5·5 million guilders a year in fuel bills, or well over a million pounds sterling.

The NMB Bank building is seriously green in its approach to energy consumption. Since the use of fossil fuels must be cut if the potentially disastrous effects of rising carbon dioxide production are to be minimised, it is important for architects to make efforts not merely to reduce the consumption of fuels, but to eliminate them altogether. The NMB Bank headquarters uses about 90% less energy than a typical office block of the 1970s. This performance is achieved by the integration of good levels of insulation in the structure plus the careful use of passive heating and ventilation backed up by sophisticated and well-controlled mechanical services.

Probably the key to the building's good performance lies in the fact that it generates its own electricity and makes use of the waste heat that is lost up the cooling towers of a conventional power station. Recent studies of a number of commercial buildings have shown that electricity can be the largest single energy use, particularly in buildings like banks that make extensive use of computers [4].

Green principles

A considerable part of the airing of green issues that has taken place to date has dealt with matters that are less well-defined than energy consumption [5]. These issues range from the essentially scientific (health hazards of materials), through the fringes of current scientific acceptability (health effects of electromagnetic radiation), to the entirely mystical (pre-figured by Christopher Alexander's pursuit of the 'quality without a name' [6]).

These less tangible aspects of the green approach are also taken on board at the NMB Bank, increasing its radicality. Ton Alberts, the architect, wanted to make a building that was open to 'etheric forces', but could not avoid the Faraday cage of reinforcing bars in the concrete structure. This protects the users from possibly harmful external radiations but does nothing to dissipate the radiation given off by all the computers. The harmful effects of electromagnetic radiation are more widely recognised in the rest of Europe, Scandinavia and the USSR than they are in the UK where, typically, nothing will be done until it can be shown that money can be made out of it.

At the Bank materials were used that showed the hand of the builder as much as possible. To see human blemishes in the painted concrete walls, in the wrought timber (from sustainable sources) used throughout as stair rails, wall claddings and ceiling finishes, and in the finely detailed external brickwork gives, in Ton Alberts' words, 'a radiation that you need for living'. A machine-finished component does not have that quality, which he describes as the same as the warmth that comes from old things. Where possible, natural paints were used to avoid the emission of harmful chemicals, and natural gypsum was specified for plaster because its level of radioactivity is far less than that emitted by man-made gypsum.

The building is also filled with specially commissioned works of art that enliven the central street. There are paintings, conventional sculpture, water sculptures, stained glass, mirrors and textiles which all add something to the space and give different areas their own quality of enclosure or connectivity. In one atrium there is a huge stone sphere over which water flows on its way to the internal planting. In another a mirror set at 45° on top of a rough stone pylon reflects a view of the sky to a similar mirror in the next atrium, sending a beam of light along the darker connecting route between the two top-lit spaces. Such individual works of art help to reinforce the presence of individual workmanship within the building.

Where this approach is less convincing is in the interior design work of some of the spaces, including the directors' dining room, which was undertaken by Pentagram. At this point the finishes are more like those one might expect to find in a purpose-made building of this type, and the hand of the individual builder is less obvious. Nevertheless, the use of natural wood and non-synthetic fabrics continues the overall philosophy of the building.

About thirty-five people from Ton Alberts' office worked on the Bank, plus ten

Left: angled columns reflect the exterior forms
Right: top-lit circulation towers are all different, but each is richly planted

(photographs: Alberts en van Huut)

or twelve consultants. The contract was let in a normal way, and the contractor, Voormolen–Heijmans–IBC of Amsterdam, realised at the start that this was to be an important building. The architect is pleased with the result: the worst error was 6mm over the total height in one of the atrium spaces, which reflects a high degree of precision in the work. (At the start of the job the contractors invested in laser technology with which to check the rake of the brickwork.) The work started on site in April 1983 and was completed in April 1987.

The NMB Bank demonstrates that a modern office block can also be a piece of green architecture, in ways that range from the technical to the philosophical. More important, it shows how a green building can be all the things that an organisation wants from a commercial point of view. As well as providing healthy working conditions for the Bank's employees and saving money on fuel bills, the new building functions as an advertisement for the Bank, whose list of customers is growing rapidly. When visited in August 1990, the building was fully booked for tourist visits for six months. There are very few banks whose head office is a tourist attraction. Its instantly recognisable form is known all over Holland, and yet it is not the form that would be expected of an institutional organisation such as a bank, who are usually noted for their traditionalism and desire to play safe.

The greatest difficulty reported by the architect was finding the right design staff. There are not many 'organic architects' (Ton Alberts' term) to be found in Holland or anywhere else, and some of those that joined the office felt that they were in Utopia, and did not need to work hard. Ton Alberts found that they were 'always a little bit flying in air'. It appeared that some designers forget that a commitment to a green philosophy does not remove the necessity for conventional graft.

The fact that the NMB Bank is the most energy-efficient building in the world is not due solely to the manipulation of building form and fabric, the areas of design with which architects are traditionally concerned. The success of the building comes from the view taken of the operation of the whole bank in this particular building on this particular site. Thus it would not be possible for staff to arrive at the building in an energy-saving way without an efficient public transport system (the bank is linked to the Metro station by a pedestrianised route).

Efficiency comes also from generating electricity for the office needs and using the waste heat from this process to maintain the temperature of the building. Then follow the systems within the building to reduce conventional energy use and subsequent carbon dioxide output, the systems to give the users control of their environment, and the use of materials in as natural a state as possible. It is this totality of approach which makes the building unique.

Nevertheless, the NMB is a bank and contains all that one expects to find in a major bank headquarters. The Bank has found that the individuality and uniqueness of the building have increased the number of customers. Investment in this quality of architecture has proved profitable and has linked the greening of buildings directly with capitalist goals. Although some may deplore this, the NMB Bank demonstrates that a built environment which radically reduces carbon dioxide output and enriches the quality of life for those who work in it need not entail a way of living which is that much different. The bank is unique in showing that the future could be here, now, for all of us.

Client: NMB Bank
Architect: Alberts en van Huut (partner in charge, Ton Alberts)
Building services engineers: Treffers & Partners
Main contractor: Voormolen–Heijmans–IBC

References

(1) Duffy F. (1988), 'The European challenge', *Architects' Journal*, 17 August 1988.

(2) NMB Bank (undated), 'NMB Bank's head office', NMB Bank Corporate PR and Publicity Department, Publications Section, Amsterdam.

(3) Holdsworth W. (1989), 'Organic services', *Building Services: the CIBSE Journal*, March 1989.

(4) Brownhill D. (1990), 'Energy efficient offices: case histories', *Building Services: the CIBSE Journal*, June 1990 pp63–64.

(5) Pearson D. (1989), *The natural house book*, Conran Octopus, London.

(6) Alexander C. et al (1979), *The timeless way of building*, Oxford University Press.

Woodhouse Medical Centre, Sheffield

In other sections of the National Health Service, the NHS itself acts as the provider of buildings, but because general practitioners and dentists are independent contractors, they are required to provide their own premises. However, in the case of doctors, there is a scheme of active encouragement to persuade them to build new surgeries, or at least rehabilitate their old ones.

Because the NHS, under the aegis of the local Family Practitioner Committees (FPC), is encouraging the building of new general practice surgeries, it follows that there will be certain criteria to be met by the designers of such surgeries. The requirements are set out in the 'bible' of general medical practice – the so-called Red Book. They cover the number, size and layout of rooms within any proposed surgery design. The functions of individual rooms and their areas are defined within close limits. Combined with a fixed percentage of circulation space, this gives a precise maximum area for any proposed building.

The approval of the room sizes, areas and interrelationships generates a budget figure based on the building area. These budgets are constant throughout the country, with no allowance for different building costs. Although they are updated, they do not seem to keep pace with tender price rises during a building boom. The one concession to the varied nature of different locations is that additional money can be claimed for what are known as 'abnormal site conditions', ie any site that is not a flat green field on which conventional

Looking towards the entrance
(photograph: Peter Lathey)

W Waiting
R Reception
L Lobby
D Dentist
C Common room
X X-ray
G Gas store
O Office
CO Consulting room
T Treatment room
F Fire exit
S Store
B Bins

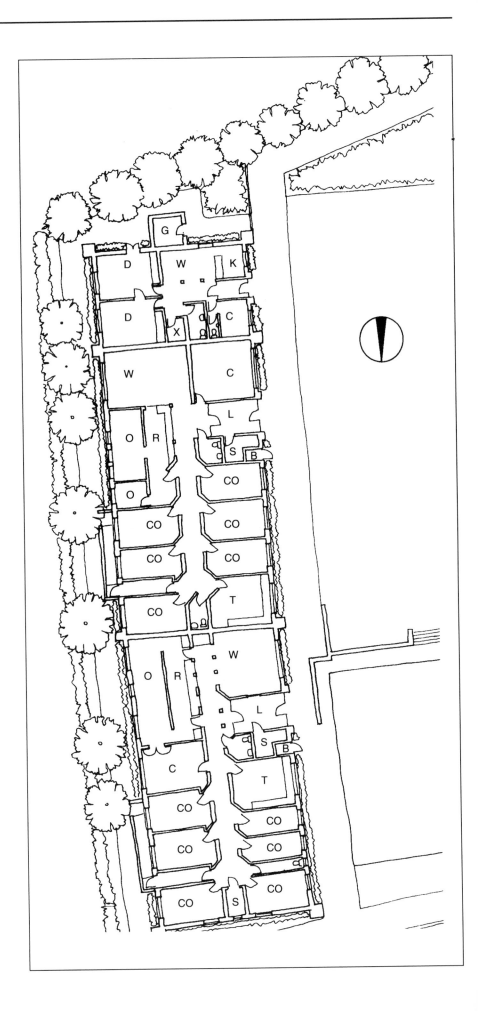

Site plan and layout

foundations can be used. At the time of building the Woodhouse Medical Centre the permitted cost worked out at about £500 per m², which is about the cost of a house of reasonable standard, and is not a large budget. Additional money was allowed for abnormal site conditions.

The overall plan

The clients for the Woodhouse Medical Centre were two separate general practices, and a dental practice. All three were practising from existing buildings which were cramped and unsatisfactory in various ways. The two medical practices had different approaches and methods of working and did not want to merge into one large practice which would lose the advantages of smaller scale, but the FPC did not want to have the cost of building separate buildings. The end result was to house the three practices in one building, with complete separation but with the advantages of shared building costs.

The site for the building, a piece of open land adjoining the public library, had to accommodate a Health Authority clinic as well as the proposed Medical Centre. To achieve the required total area of 650m² (all on one level to allow full access for disabled patients) plus the number of parking spaces required by the planning authority, resulted in the footprint for the proposed Medical Centre being a long thin rectangle running north–south adjacent to the eastern boundary of the site, where a beech hedge separated it from some four-storey local authority flats. The proposed site sloped from south to north, with a total fall of 3m over its length of roughly 60m.

Within this 12m-wide rectangle the various rooms were arranged along a central corridor 1,500mm in width. To avoid any sense of being cut off from the outside and to provide natural daylighting, the ceiling of the corridor was opened up to the underside of the roof, allowing daylight to enter through rooflights. This simple structural strategy allowed the long external walls and the walls either side of the corridor to carry beams which would support half trusses, each truss covering a room with a span of about 5m, with the flat ceilings of the rooms fixed to the underside of the trusses.

Above the corridor where the ceiling was omitted, rafters were used to connect together the tops of the trusses. The vertical sides of the trusses in the corridor were splayed back to increase the open feel of the corridor. Its walls were vertical to door height but widened out above this level to admit more light. This also allowed light to be introduced into the backs of the rooms by glazing between the trusses and forming light wells into the flat ceilings to correspond to the positions of the rooflights.

The choice of materials

The primary decision was to make the form of the building uncomplicated. With a limited budget there would be little money for complex roof forms or expensive materials; the building would have to be a simple shed. The decision was also made to use load-bearing brickwork with glue-laminated softwood timber for the load-bearing elements. This was for various reasons, the first of which was cost.

However, the use of brick and timber has other advantages for an architect trying to respond to environmental concerns. Although the extraction and processing of clay into bricks requires a certain amount of energy, brick can be classed as a 'medium' energy material, meaning that it does not represent a

Aerated concrete blocks are used in the footings to try to minimise cold bridging at the floor edge, and the 150mm water-repellent glass fibre insulation in the wall is taken down below the bottom of the under-floor insulation for the same reason.

Weepholes and gravel backfill allow accumulated water to drain from the cavity. Under the slab is 150mm expanded polystyrene insulation.

At the window opening cold bridging is avoided by the use of two separate lintels of glulam timber joined by beech dowels. Plastic extrusions provide the necessary vertical and horizontal damp proof courses round the opening.

The window is built in with stainless steel cramps as far back in the wall as possible, both to protect it and to provide visual modelling of the wall surface.

The roof trusses bolted to the lintels carry the vapour barrier, which is sealed to the outer face of the wall behind a softwood fascia.

Spacing screws with timber struts carry the outer roof while allowing space for the 350mm mineral fibre insulation.

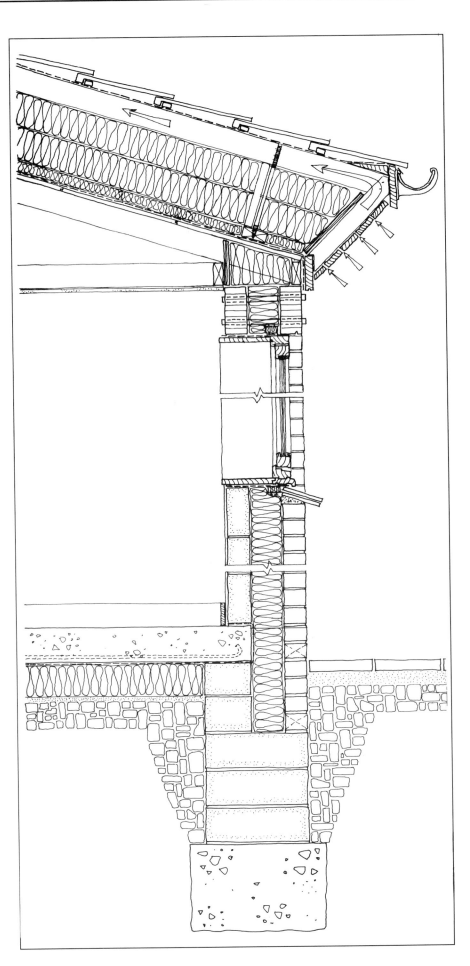

Typical section at eaves

large amount of energy in production [1]. Since the reduction of fossil fuel consumption is the single most important aspect of green architecture, it is essential for designers to consider the energy needed to make the materials that they specify. Brick and timber were eminently suited for the small, almost domestic scale, spans involved in a medical centre.

Another reason for the choice of load-bearing brickwork for the external walls was familiarity. Masonry construction is common in the UK, and the architects wanted to present the contractor with as few problems as possible. The Code of Practice for masonry construction [2] allows a cavity width of 150mm before the two leaves of the wall are no longer considered to be acting as a composite structure. This cavity width, filled with resin-bonded water-repellent glass fibre batts, was chosen for the proposed building, giving a U-value of 0·2 W/m²K (three times that required by the Building Regulations of the time). A masonry cavity wall, even with a cavity wider than normal, is still a construction technique familiar to a UK contractor.

Timber, in the form of glue-laminated softwood, was the choice for load-bearing members for the same energy reasons that brick was used; the production of a kilogram of structural timber uses less energy than is required to produce any other structural material [3]. Glulam was preferred over other timber types for several reasons, of which the most obvious is that it comes from farmed trees that are regularly replanted, not from virgin forests.

Timber has further advantages. When a tree grows, it uses the carbon dioxide in the atmosphere: carbon is taken out of the air and turned into the structure of the tree. If that tree is made into packaging or newspaper or some other ephemeral product, the carbon is put back into the air when the material is burned or when it rots. If the tree is used as part of the structure of a building, the carbon it has extracted from the air will be locked up in the building where it will be kept from returning to the atmosphere. It has been proposed that a considerable increase in the use of timber in buildings, which would encourage the planting of more trees, would be one strategy for taking carbon dioxide out of the atmosphere [4].

The roof covering was specified as concrete slates so as to match the roofs of the adjoining flats, to use little energy in production and, most important, to save money. Although the tiles chosen were low cost, they are expected to last as long as more expensive versions.

In the case of the facing bricks, the highly insulated nature of the walls meant that very little heat would leak from the inside to keep the bricks warm in cold weather. It was therefore considered essential to use frost-resistant FL grade bricks so that the outer leaf of the wall could freeze without damage. It was then a case of finding bricks of the right grade and cost that were available locally to minimise the need for road transport to site with its obvious environmental and energy penalties.

Because a green building needs money spending on additional insulation and to achieve energy conservation, the specification of other items has to be tightly controlled by criteria that are essentially technical rather than aesthetic. In a green building there is little room for architectural extravagances.

The ground floor construction is a reinforced concrete slab spanning from the external walls to the central corridor walls. The fill beneath it acts as support for the insulation under the slab and as permanent shuttering for the casting of the slab, but if it were to move it would have no effect on the support of the floor.

Reinforced concrete is not a completely satisfactory material for use in a green building. Although it has a relatively low energy content it is difficult to recycle when the building's useful life is over. The use of waste concrete as hardcore is a worthwhile recycling activity which avoids the extraction and transport of new materials, but the re-use of materials in a less degraded form is preferable. However, for the ground floor of a building, it is hard to find a more suitable material.

Softwood was used for window frames as well as structure. This is grown in Europe, so transport costs (and energy costs) are less than for timbers from the other side of the world, and all softwoods are grown as farmed crops, with replanting following felling. The replacement in Britain of natural deciduous forests or moorland by managed conifer forests for softwood supply is not an unmitigated blessing in ecological terms, in that the variety of wildlife species is greatly reduced in the new forests. The counter-argument is that the UK at present relies on imports for 90% of its timber supplies, and the use of home grown timber should therefore be encouraged in terms of both energy and employment. There are few easy answers in the attempt to create an environmentally-responsive architecture.

The use of softwood from whatever source for window frames means that toxic preservatives will be necessary to protect it and to kill the fungi and insects that attack wood, although the siting of the window in the wall will affect the degree of exposure and hence the durability of the wood. The timber lintels were preserved by the use of solid rods of boron inserted into holes drilled near the ends of the lintels. Boron is one of the least toxic preservatives, and the rods remain in a solid form safely out of contact with the environment until the timber attains a moisture content that might allow rot to develop. If this happens, the boron dissolves into the wood, providing protection where needed. The holes to take the rods are plugged with small dowels which can be withdrawn to allow the preservative rods to be checked or replaced at any time.

The energy strategy

The principal objective in making the Woodhouse Medical Centre a green building was to minimise its use of fossil fuel energy. It is not easy to exploit passive solar energy gains in a surgery building, because using large areas of south-facing glazing generates problems of security and privacy. The site requirements meant that the building's long axis had to run north–south, which made it difficult to obtain solar gains.

It was decided to give the building a thermally heavy construction to enable it to absorb casual heat gains such as through windows and rooflights. However, a waiting room occupied by forty 'flu patients could represent an energy gain of 5kW, and unless the structure was designed to absorb such a gain, the area could overheat, given that 5kW is roughly the peak space heating demand for one unit of the building.

To avoid this, insulation was positioned round the outside of a heavy

The deep eaves and thickness of roof insulation

(photograph: Peter Lathey)

structure, thus providing a mass to store heat and even out temperature variations. The floor slab alone represented 100m³ of thermal storage. All internal partitions were also made of brick to provide additional mass. The massive structure has the added advantage that it provides good sound-proofing between rooms, and heavy doors are used to enhance this important aspect of the design.

The roof

The largest single heat-losing element in the building was the roof, so it was desirable to incorporate a high level of insulation in this element. It was decided to put the insulation in the plane of the roof to avoid the creation of cold voids in attics which would need to be sealed from the building. Given a warm attic, all storage tanks and service runs could run in the void without special protection. When used with a pitched roof this approach also avoids the potential cold bridge problem that can occur with a cold attic directly above a heated space, where heat could pass directly through the inner leaf of the wall from the room to the cold space.

It was decided to attempt to make the roof U-value less than 0·1 W/m²K, which would entail insulation of about 350mm of mineral fibre. The novel design developed for the Medical Centre sought to solve three problems:

- the fixing of the vapour barrier;
- the avoidance of cold bridges; and
- the incorporation of any desired thickness of insulation.

The cost of the roof also had to be affordable. The overall solution was to create a double roof that would allow the formation of a void to contain the insulation.

The first part of the roof construction was to install conventional gang-nailed softwood trusses at 600mm centres, incorporating wind bracing as for a conventional truss roof. On top of the trusses a decking of water-repellent chipboard was fixed. The glues used in chipboard manufacture are thought to be hazardous to health [5], but the deck was exposed to a sealed roof void rather than to an inhabited space. Water-repellent chipboard was specified in case it rained before the deck was covered in by the roof construction.

Over the deck was laid a Swedish vapour barrier of reinforced polythene. In this case the use of an imported material was justified by its superior performance; there was no British product to match it. Part of the attraction of the material is that the manufacturers supply a special double-sided tape of great tenacity, which simplifies the achievement of a good seal at all joints and junctions [6].

The role of the vapour barrier is as much to do with reducing air movement through the building as it is with cutting vapour transmission and condensation. In a highly insulated building the heat loss due to unwanted ventilation or draughts is the greatest single cause of heat losses as the insulation value of the structural elements of the building rises. Although a plastered masonry wall offers good resistance to air movement, where there is any kind of frame structure such as a roof, a vapour barrier (or, more accurately, an air-vapour barrier) must be incorporated. Care was also taken to seal the vapour barrier to the external walls to prevent air ingress at the junction of two elements. The polythene was turned down the wall and fixed to it with tape to form a continuous seal.

The decked-over trusses with their vapour barrier covering formed a waterproof enclosure to the building which allowed work to continue inside while the roof was completed. The next step was to construct a second roof 350mm above the decking to carry the roof tiles; the gap between the two could then be filled with insulation. The outer roof was formed with 50 x 100mm rafters at 600mm centres in the normal way, and these were fixed to the lower roof with spacing screws. The German-made screws with threads at both ends allowed the rafters to be fixed accurately at the correct distance from the lower roof. To provide a fixing for the lower ends of the screws, 50 x 150mm timber bearers running horizontally along the roof were nailed through the decking to the trusses. Penetration of the vapour barrier by the nails was not a problem, because the polythene barrier was trapped between the bearers and the decking, forming an effective seal. The spacing screws were given additional rigidity in compression by the insertion of simple spacers of 50 x 50mm softwood between the upper rafters and the horizontal bearers.

To improve the rigidity of the roof even further, the rafters were fixed at the upper end of the roof near the ridge to a leg formed by extending the end chord of the truss. The roof was surprisingly rigid when constructed, and was stiffened further by the tiling battens of 25 x 38mm softwood fixed to the upper rafters in the normal way. The use of the spacing screws was suggested by the structural engineer as a means of creating the space needed for the roof insulation.

The insulation was put in in three layers and fitted round the screws and spacers without difficulty, and the full rafter depth of 100mm was left as a ventilation space, open at the eaves and with a dry fixed ventilated ridge to allow a flow of air to carry off any moisture that might penetrate the tiles and underslating felt. The choice of insulation material was mineral fibre, a material that is low in cost, moderate in terms of the energy needed to manufacture it, and made from materials that are not scarce.

There is some concern that the use of a fibrous material could have health implications, particularly for building workers, just as happened with asbestos. At the time the building was designed, the available information was that asbestos fibres could split along their length to form fibres of narrow diameters, whereas mineral fibres split across to form short lengths. Since fibre diameter is seen as the deciding factor in lung damage, and since mineral fibres are extruded at fixed diameters considerably greater than those known to be harmful, mineral fibres are assumed to be safe for use [7].

External walls

The construction of the external walls was straighforward compared with the roof. The maximum cavity width was fixed at 150mm by the Code of Practice, so this was the width employed. Stainless steel twist-type wall ties were used at 450mm centres vertically and horizontally. The ties were made in Sheffield and supplied ex-stock. The outer leaf of the wall was brick and the inner leaf was a water-resistant lightweight concrete block, chosen more for its ability to resist any water penetration of the wall than for its insulating properties. The insulation of resin-bonded glass fibre treated with water repellant was used to fill the cavity completely, avoiding the need to keep it free from mortar droppings and any possibility of the insulation in a partially filled cavity falling forward to touch the outer leaf and conduct water across.

Wall ties are an obvious cold bridge, and ties of some non-conducting material were considered preferable. Danish ties made of glass reinforced plastic and suitable for cavity widths of up to 300mm were a possibility, but would have required a lengthy consultation and calculation procedure with no guarantee that the local Building Control Officers would permit their use. It seemed more appropriate to try to build an ecological building within the terms of the existing UK Building Regulations to see what could be achieved without having to obtain special waivers. The wall as constructed has a U-value of about 0·2 W/m²K.

Glazing

The performance of glazing can be improved by increasing the number of panes, but this in turn increases the thickness and cost of the window frame. The solution adopted at Woodhouse was to use double glazing to avoid the need for expensive window frames, but to alter the construction of the double glazing units.

The unit specified was two panes of 4mm glass separated by a 12mm cavity, but both panes of glass had a microscopically thin low-emissivity coating to reflect

The daylit central corridor

(photograph: Peter Lathey)

heat back into the building. The cavity was filled with argon gas (which is less conductive than air), giving a unit 20mm thick, but with the thermal performance of a quadruple unit (U-value 1·6 W/m²K). This is a satisfactory performance for a transparent element, but the windows are still about ten times poorer thermally than the walls, although they cost ten times as much per square metre. The cost of the special units was less than the cost of thicker frames.

Windows present another energy advantage in that they provide daylight and reduce the need for electric light. Daylight allows doctors to see clearly the condition of their patients, and makes an important contribution to the quality of the building. The generous levels of daylight admitted to the rooms and corridors generate a sense of well-being for patients and occupants, and this is as important an aspect of the building's green strategy as the saving of fossil fuels.

The floor

The floor insulation was 150mm expanded polystyrene, chosen partly on cost grounds and partly because it was one of the few underfloor insulants that do not use CFCs in their manufacture. The insulation is laid between the hardcore and the slab and acts as permanent shuttering to the concrete. The slab itself is 150mm thick with a power-floated finish to allow the floor to be laid directly without additional screeds. The overall floor U-value is approximately 0·2 W/m²K. This thickness of insulation led to one of the few supply problems for the contractor, who found it difficult to obtain all the expanded polystyrene at one time.

Cold bridges and how to avoid them

Great care was taken to minimise the problem of cold bridging. There was a potential problem at the perimeter, but the wall insulation was taken down below dpc level (the cavity fill material is approved for this purpose because of its water-repellent properties) so as to meet the underfloor insulation. Below this level, the wall was formed in 350mm-thick insulated concrete blocks designed for underground use (the thickness compensating to some extent for the fact that they are a less effective insulator than glass fibre).

In the walls there were two potentially serious cold bridging problems, the first being the opening itself. Normally at the jambs the inner blockwork would be returned to meet the outer leaf, but in a wall with 150mm of insulation the block, even if of low density concrete, would be an appreciably less efficient insulator than the remainder of the wall. The cold bridge effect might not be serious enough to allow condensation to occur, but it would reduce the overall insulation value of the wall.

The solution adopted was to have no return at all on the blockwork and use a proprietary plastic extrusion fixed to the window frames as a dpc and finish to the outer leaf of the wall. The extrusion provided a method of sealing the window frame to the brickwork, and the cavity on the inside of the reveal was then closed with a wooden lining backed by a vapour barrier sealed to the window frame and to the inner blockwork.

It is always important to achieve airtight construction in a low energy building, and openings involving the junction of dissimilar components are difficult to manage. The big disadvantage of using the plastic extrusion was that although it would provide an effective seal and dpc at openings, it was filled with polyurethane insulation (to prevent cold bridging at reveals) and therefore presumably contained CFCs. At the time it seemed the most effective way of dealing with the problem, but further work is needed to find an environmentally benign, airtight reveal detail that solves the cold bridging problem.

Another problem associated with openings has to do with lintels. The conventional technique in cavity wall construction is to use some form of steel lintel to carry the wall over openings. This is cheap and effective, but it forms an obvious cold bridge due to the high thermal conductivity of the steel. The solution adopted at the Medical Centre was to use separate inner and outer lintels and to provide cavity trays above them to throw water to the outer face of the wall. The lintels were made of glue-laminated softwood 100mm thick and 215mm deep. The outer one was given additional protection by a drip formed of creasing tiles to deflect water in locations where the lintel was not protected by a roof overhang. The timber lintels were joined together for increased rigidity by dowel pegs (of European beech, not tropical hardwood) and the 150mm gap between them was filled with insulation as used in the walls.

The only clearly visible result of the building's superinsulated construction is the design of the eaves. A large roof overhang was required to protect the windows and wooden lintels from the effects of the weather. It was achieved without any significant reduction in the amount of sky visible through the windows by sloping the eaves up at 45 degrees from the face of the external wall at the level of the chipboard deck, to meet a fascia carried on the rafters whose upper face is 450mm above this deck. Combined with a 150mm diameter rainwater gutter, this gives an overhang of more than 600mm. The sloping part of the eaves is clad with timber boarding, fixed with small gaps that allow ventilation of the 100mm air space above the insulation, and this boarding is a clear visual expression of the abnormal roof thickness. At the ends of the building, the sloped eaves combine visually with the slope of the buttresses to link roof and wall, and the corners are further accentuated by the use of large corbelled 'capitals' at the tops of the buttresses, made of clay creasing tiles.

Heating and ventilation

The insulation incorporated into the design resulted in a reduction of heating requirements (according to the architects' calculations) of about 75% of what would have resulted if the Medical Centre had been constructed in accordance with the Building Regulations of the time. Part of this reduction was achieved by the use of a Swedish heat recovery ventilation system in each unit. This extracts stale air from the rooms and passes it through a heat exchanger, where its heat is used to warm incoming fresh air which is supplied to the rooms through ducts in the roof space. The net effect is to allow an air change rate of one per hour, but to give the heat loss equivalent of only about 0·3 air changes per hour. This is important in a superinsulated building, because the heat lost by ventilation would otherwise be the largest element in the total heat loss calculation. The ventilation unit is controlled by a rheostat allowing the users to adjust the rate as required according to conditions in the building.

The low heating requirement allowed each 275m² unit to be heated by a small domestic wall-hung boiler. In this respect the green technology of the building actually saved money, as the heating installation was four times smaller than that needed for a conventional building. The adjoining Health Authority clinic, although only about one third the size of the Medical Centre, and built at the same time, has a plant room of about 10m²; in the Medical Centre the boilers are hung on the walls in cupboards, one to each unit.

The boilers are gas-fired to give the lowest CO_2 output per unit of heat produced, and they condense the flue gases to extract more heat, giving an increase in efficiency of 10–15% over a conventional gas boiler. To allow the boilers to operate as often as possible in the condensing mode, the radiators have a low water content to allow fast response, are fitted with individual thermostatic valves, and are slightly oversized. Combined with the long pipe runs, this helps to keep return water temperatures low. There is no chance of Legionnaires' Disease as the entire system is sealed and pressurised, with no open supply tanks. The special radiators were more expensive than conventional panel radiators, but this was a case of money being spent to enhance performance. Pipework is run in the insulated roof space where it is also lagged to reduce heat loss.

The boilers provide the other clue to the low energy nature of the building, as they emit characteristic plumes of vapour from the flue terminals when operating in condensing mode. Overall the insulation, controlled ventilation and condensing boilers are designed to reduce the space heating energy demand by about 80% compared with a conventional building.

The hot water supply presented the architects with difficult choices. A doctors' surgery needs hot water supplied to nearly every room, although the requirement for hot water at any time is small, most of it being a matter of frequent hand rinsing. A hot water system using the gas boiler to heat an insulated cylinder would normally be the most efficient solution, but the long thin nature of the plan meant that users would run off a lot of cold water before hot water came through from a central supply – although there was no way of knowing how much.

The decision was therefore taken to provide electric undersink hot water storage units to supply small amounts of water with minimum losses. The disadvantage is the low efficiency of the conversion of primary energy to electricity, which means that the system chosen may be less efficient in overall energy terms (and in terms of CO_2 production) than a centralised gas system. Once again it was a case of making a decision that seemed reasonable on the basis of the known facts at the time.

Lighting is by means of compact fluorescent fittings to try to achieve the visual quality of incandescent lamps, but with an 80% energy saving. In some cases the diffusers supplied with fittings reduced the manufacturer's stated light output to such an extent that additional fittings had to be installed after the building was occupied. The low budget limited the choice of fittings; the expensive bowl-shaped uplighters were used sparingly for maximum effect. The lighting policy was carried throughout the building and compact fluorescent bulbs were used even in the adjustable wall lamps for examinations.

Some attempt was made to specify materials of natural origin, as much for their visual qualities as for their environmental impact. The floor finishes were cork tiles, and carpets were of wool and animal hair. Curtains were made of natural fibres, but the paints and stains were conventional. Fitted furniture was of softwood blockboard rather than hardwoods or chipboards, or particle boards containing formaldehyde binders.

The Woodhouse Medical Centre is a serious attempt to demonstrate that a green building need not cost more than a normal one. It uses environmentally benign materials and cuts energy demand by 80%, but it was built within the fixed, and not very generous, budget allowed for a conventional building. If all buildings were built, or retrofitted, to this specification, the UK could reduce its energy consumption, and hence its CO_2 emissions, by 40%. If nothing else, the Woodhouse Medical Centre demonstrates that governments cannot refuse to act to reduce greenhouse gas emissions on the grounds that such action would be too expensive; on the contrary, it can be said that not acting will cost the earth.

Clients: Woodhouse Medical Centre Co.
Architects and energy consultants: Brenda and Robert Vale
Contractor: Wildgoose Construction Ltd.

References

(1) Szokolay S. (1980), *Environmental Science Handbook*, The Architectural Press, London.

(2) British Standards Institute (1978), *BS 5628 Code of Practice for the structural use of masonry, Part 1: Unreinforced masonry*, BSI, London.

(3) Szokolay (1980), *op. cit.*

(4) Marland G. (1988), 'The prospect of solving the CO_2 problem through global reforestation', *DoE/NBB0082*, US Department of Energy, February.

(5) Curwell S., March C., and Venables R. (Eds.) (1990), *Buildings and Health: the Rosehaugh Guide to the design, construction, use and management of buildings*, RIBA Publications, London.

(6) Monarflex Ltd. (undated), *Reinforced quality* (information folder), Monarflex Ltd., St. Albans.

(7) Curwell S., March C. (1986), *Hazardous building materials: a guide to the selection of alternatives*, E. & F. N. Spon, London.